By Accident or Design

1 Waiting for Treatment

2 Minding the Quality

3 Working with Other Specialties

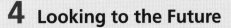

4 Looking to the Future

Contents

© Crown Copyright 1996

Applications for reproduction should be
made to HMSO

Typeset by Ministry of Design, Bath

Printed in the UK for the Audit Commission
by Colourcraft, Cardiff

ISBN 011 886 436 X

London: HMSO

Photographs by kind permission of: Network
(cover picture, p3): Hilary Shedel (p10, p22,
p24, p27, p33, p36, p51, p55,): Impact (p48):
Abigail Moore (p61).

With thanks to the staff and patients of West
Middlesex University Hospital NHS Trust,
Isleworth, and St Mary's NHS Trust,
Paddington.

Preface

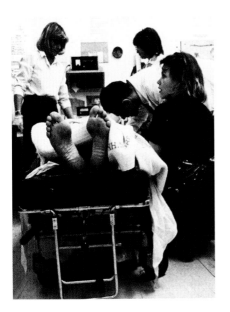

The Audit Commission is responsible for the external audit of NHS trusts and other health service bodies in England and Wales. As part of its function, the Commission is charged with reviewing the economy, efficiency and effectiveness of services provided by those bodies. To do so, studies and audits of selected topics are undertaken each year.

This study concerns the initial provision of emergency care to patients in an acute general hospital setting. While much of it deals with the running of accident and emergency (A&E) departments, it recognises that these occupy a pivotal position between community and secondary care; to function effectively and efficiently they require the support and co-operation of a wide range of specialties and support services, both within and beyond the hospital. Health commissioners have a key role to play in co-ordinating these services and setting the framework within which they operate.

This report is aimed at trust boards and directors, both managers and clinicians, and at purchasers of A&E services. It examines the extent of change since the National Audit Office reported on A&E departments in 1992 (Refs. 1, 2) and on key reports, such as that of the Clinical Standards Advisory Group (Ref. 3) on emergency hospital admissions. The recommendations made in those reports are summarised in Appendices 3 and 4. It identifies the steps that need to be taken to improve the provision of care to all who are currently examined or treated in A&E departments and how these requirements may change as alternative settings for the provision of emergency care develop.

The study on which this report is based was carried out by Ian Jones and Penelope Cummins with advice from Fionna Moore (Consultant in Accident and Emergency Medicine) and under the general direction of Joanne Shaw, Ken Sneath and Jonathan Boyce. The study was supported by an advisory group (Appendix 1). The Audit Commission is grateful to all individuals and organisations who assisted. Responsibility for the content and conclusions rests solely with the Audit Commission.

Introduction

'...a high profile department at the interface between community and hospital care...'

1. Each year, patients make almost 15 million visits to accident and emergency (A&E) departments in England and Wales. These departments have a high public profile as they see more new patients than any other hospital department and feature regularly in the news and in television drama. They occupy a pivotal position in the NHS, forming one of the principal interfaces between community and hospital care. Many A&E departments also act as the 'front door' of the hospital, receiving patients referred by GPs to inpatient specialties for emergency hospital admission.

2. Until the 1960s, 'casualty' units used to be managed by 'caretaker' consultants from other specialties, often orthopaedics. The Platt Report (Ref. 4) signalled a change of name and status. Most A&E departments[I] are now headed by at least one specialist A&E consultant.

3. There are 227 A&E departments in England and Wales which treat all types of injuries and medical emergencies and which, with a few exceptions, are open 24 hours per day. Most treat an average of 70 to 200 new patients each day, although some in remote areas are considerably smaller, and a few 'giants' see over 300 per day.

4. A&E departments in England and Wales cost about £600 million each year. Unit costs based on official financial returns vary widely between trusts (Exhibit 1), but the amount of variation is almost certainly exaggerated by a number of factors:

◆ the figures do not take account of differences in A&E case mix (which are hard to quantify);

◆ many trusts include minor injuries units or peripheral A&E departments in their costs;

◆ A&E attendance figures may be inaccurately reported;

◆ the costs of support services such as radiology, pathology and pharmacy are often allocated between departments on an historical basis, and so fail to reflect actual levels of use; and

◆ allocation of trust overheads, including site capital charges, may distort comparisons.

These factors (which are elaborated in Appendix 2) make interpretation of individual departments' unit costs unreliable. But, equally, they are unlikely to explain all of the variations observed between trusts. Moreover, observable differences in the productivity of both nurses and doctors suggest real differences in efficiency. If all departments could match the most efficient, resources could be made available to improve service levels or quality. It is the aim of this report and the associated audits to help trusts achieve this.

I
Throughout this report, the term 'A&E department' is used to refer only to those which describe themselves as 'major units' receiving '999' ambulances and offering the full range of accident and emergency care. It excludes 'peripheral' and minor injuries units with limited opening hours and typically staffed solely by nurses, GPs or hospital doctors on rotation from other specialties or locations.

Exhibit 1
A&E specialty costs per attendance

Unit costs appear to vary widely
between trusts.

A&E expenditure per attendance 1994/95 (£)

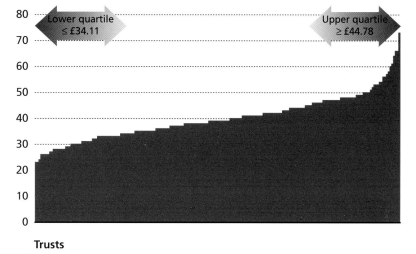

Trusts

*Source: Financial returns to Department of
Health – data for 207 trusts with one or more
non-specialist A&E departments*

Characteristics of the A&E workload

5. A&E departments primarily offer:

♦ immediate resuscitation;

♦ co-ordination of a range of services for treating severe trauma;

♦ a diagnostic service for all who attend;

♦ assessment and referral of patients who may require admission (or specialist care) to the appropriate department; and

♦ the definitive care of emergencies and also minor injuries.

6. They also provide treatment for patients seeking urgent medical advice or care who are unable, at the time, to make use of General Practitioner facilities (Ref. 5). There is considerable debate as to whether those who attend with less urgent conditions should be encouraged to seek attention elsewhere and, if so, how. However, this report concentrates on the services provided to *all* patients who *currently* use A&E services in acute general hospitals.

7. Patients attend A&E departments with a wide range of conditions, and all A&E departments face considerable uncertainty as to the volume and nature of the demands to which they will have to respond at any time. In contrast to the widespread perception, less than half of 1 per cent of A&E patients have life-threatening injuries. Considerably more need urgent attention for acute medical conditions. On average, about 15 per cent of A&E patients need to be admitted immediately as inpatients. In addition, many A&E departments receive the vast majority of patients referred by GPs for emergency hospital admission; such patients, who form up to 17 per cent of the total attendance at some A&E departments, are normally seen by a doctor from an inpatient specialty, rather than by an A&E doctor.

8. The most common complaints treated in A&E departments are cuts, bruises and grazes, followed by sprains, fractures and dislocations. Ten broad categories of conditions account for three-quarters of A&E attendances (Exhibit 2). The majority of attenders are discharged home, or into the care of their GP, after examination, tests, treatment or advice; but about one in ten patients is asked to return to a specialist outpatient clinic and a similar number, on average, are followed up in A&E clinics. However, there can be big differences between hospitals, both in the mix of accidents and emergencies treated and in the proportions of A&E patients admitted, referred or discharged (Exhibit 3).

Exhibit 2
Why patients attend A&E

Ten broad categories of conditions account for three-quarters of A&E attendances.

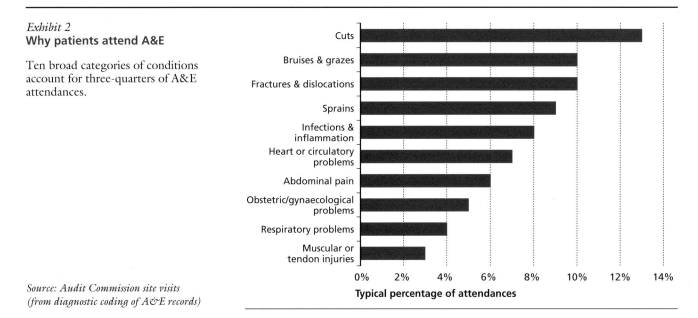

Source: Audit Commission site visits (from diagnostic coding of A&E records)

Exhibit 3
Destination of A&E patients

There are big differences between hospitals in the proportions of A&E patients admitted, referred or discharged.

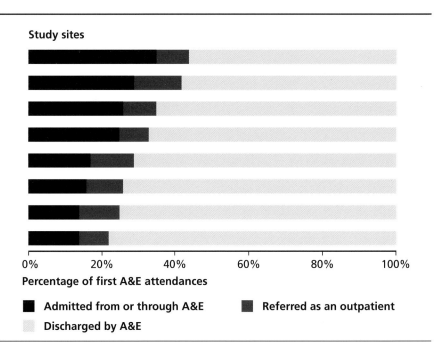

Source: Audit Commission site visits

9. The number of new A&E attendances has risen by an average 2 per cent per year since 1981, with considerable local variation. However, the total number of attendances has changed less than this because, as alternative facilities available in general practice have improved, fewer patients are being asked by A&E departments to re-attend for follow-up treatment or review (Exhibit 4). Nationally, return attendances now account for less than 14 per cent of total A&E numbers.

10. In many hospitals, medical and surgical emergencies are admitted to the wards through the A&E department. The most pronounced recent change in A&E workload has been caused by a rapid rise in the number of these admissions, which now account for 15 per cent of attendances (Exhibit 5 and Box A, overleaf). Many of these patients are acutely ill, placing a disproportionate demand on A&E nursing resources, especially if admission is delayed.

Exhibit 4
Trends in A&E workload

The number of new A&E attendances has risen by an average 2 per cent per year, but fewer patients are being asked to re-attend.

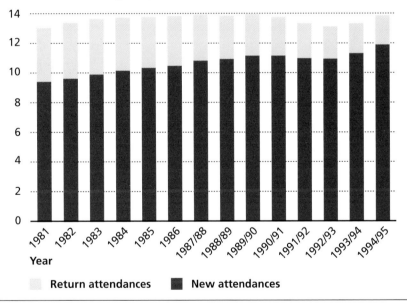

A&E attendances, England (millions)

Source: Department of Health

Exhibit 5
Increase in emergency admissions through A&E departments

The most pronounced recent change in A&E workload has been caused by a rapid rise in the number of emergency admissions through A&E.

Admissions through A&E (000s)

1,980

1,930

1,880

1,830

1,780

1,730

1989/90   1990/91   1991/92   1992/93   1993/94

Year

— **Admissions through A&E** ➡ ◀ 15% of all A&E attenders

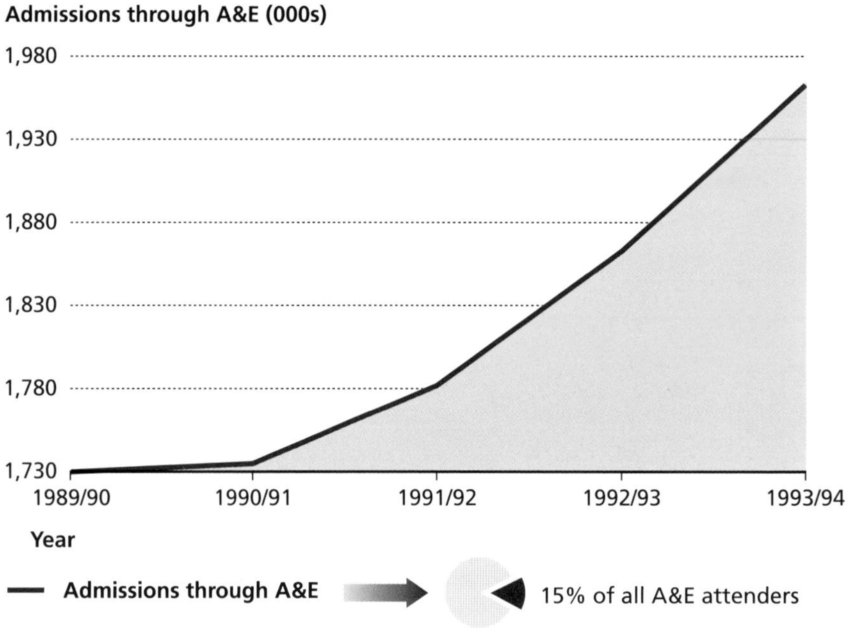

Source: Department of Health

Box A
The increase in medical and surgical emergency admissions

Reasons

Emergency hospital episodes rose by 16 per cent between 1988/89 and 1993/94, and at many hospitals there were similar increases in the numbers of patients admitted through A&E departments. There is no single explanation for this trend; a combination of clinical, environmental and social factors, increased patient expectations, and possibly even financial incentives or medico-legal pressures for GPs to refer more patients as emergencies has been suggested. However, the most marked increases in emergency admissions have been confined to relatively few medical conditions, including ill-defined chest pains and respiratory problems (Ref. 6).

Consequences

Pressures on A&E departments arise not only from the increasing *numbers* of patients referred as medical or surgical emergencies but also from the *length of time* that these patients have to wait in A&E before they can be admitted to a ward. What is more, fewer beds are now available for inpatients (partly because of the growth in elective day surgery) and so emergency patients are filling an increasing proportion of the total beds available in hospital wards. Fluctuations in the daily demand for beds are therefore greater in relation to the number of beds and consequently, in many hospitals, it is becoming more difficult to ensure swift admission.

'As a result of recent growth in workload and rising expectations, most A&E departments are experiencing pressure of demand at a time when it is increasingly difficult to recruit enough doctors.'

11. Partly as a result of this recent growth in workload, which has not always been reflected in funding, and partly because of the rising patient expectations about waiting times and quality of care, most A&E departments are experiencing pressure of demand at a time when they are finding it increasingly difficult to recruit enough doctors.

―――――

12. The next three chapters examine aspects of this demand and the problems of trying to meet it:

♦ long waiting times for A&E treatment (Chapter 1);

♦ concerns about the quality and appropriateness of treatment (Chapter 2); and

♦ delays in reaching a hospital bed (Chapter 3).

Finally, Chapter 4 looks beyond A&E departments as currently configured to the strategic questions that are increasingly being asked, such as: 'how many A&E departments should there ideally be (and where)?', and even 'should there be A&E departments at all, or is some other arrangement of emergency services preferable?'

1 Waiting for Treatment

Waiting times for A&E treatment vary markedly between hospitals and are of major concern to patients. A national framework of performance indicators and locally agreed targets are needed.

Many A&E departments could reduce congestion, roster staff more responsively to patient needs, give nurses a broader role so that patients are seen with less delay, and improve the information systems needed for effective management.

13. Surveys typically show that what patients would most like to change about A&E departments is the length of time that they are kept waiting. Waiting, and the associated uncertainty and discomfort, are irritating to those with minor injuries and to accompanying relatives. For more seriously ill or injured patients, waiting can also affect the clinical outcome. And although it is almost unknown for patients with life-threatening illnesses or injuries to wait to be seen and for treatment to start, there may be subsequent delays in completing the treatment.

Variation in waiting times

I

This is the only national indicator of speed of treatment that is relevant to *all* A&E patients. A second indicator introduced in 1995/96, which applies only to those who are admitted as inpatients, is discussed under 'trolley waits' in Chapter 3.

14. The Patient's Charter implicitly recognises the importance of reducing waiting times. It states that people attending A&E units 'should be seen immediately and their need for treatment assessed by a doctor or a nurse' (Ref. 7). Figures are published showing the percentage of patients assessed by a 'triage nurse' within five minutes of entering each A&E department.[1] *However, promptness of initial assessment is not necessarily related to how soon treatment commences or is completed.* Although one-quarter of the departments studied had both high Patient's Charter A&E ratings for 1993/94 and short waits for treatment, others that returned comparatively 'good' Patient's Charter ratings were found to be among the slowest in actually treating and discharging patients (Exhibit 6).

Exhibit 6
Speed of initial assessment compared with promptness of A&E treatment

Departments with the 'best' Patient's Charter ratings were often slow in treating and discharging patients.

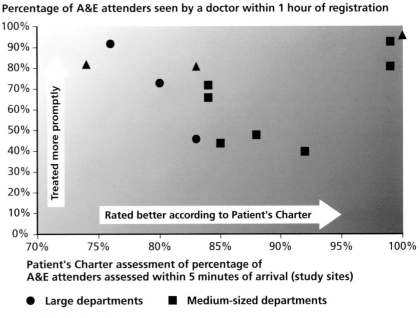

Percentage of A&E attenders seen by a doctor within 1 hour of registration

Treated more promptly

Rated better according to Patient's Charter

Patient's Charter assessment of percentage of A&E attenders assessed within 5 minutes of arrival (study sites)

● **Large departments**   ■ **Medium-sized departments**

▲ **Small departments**

Source: Patient's Charter 1993/94 league tables and data from study sites

15. The Audit Commission's measurements show big differences between hospitals in waiting time before seeing a doctor or a nurse who could treat them (Exhibit 7a). At one A&E department studied, 95 per cent of new patients were being seen within one hour, but at another the figure was only 32 per cent. There were similar variations in the total time that patients spent in A&E departments (Exhibit 7b). In some, the *majority* of A&E patients waited well over two hours before they were discharged. On a busy day, delays could be far longer.

16. Waits to see an A&E doctor can vary markedly by time of day. They can be as long in the early hours of the morning, when there are fewer patients but also fewer staff and no senior presence in the department, as at the busiest times of the day (Exhibit 8). For the same reasons, long waits are also common at weekends in many hospitals.

Exhibit 7
Promptness of A&E treatment

There are big differences between the hospitals studied in waiting time before patients see a doctor and before treatment is completed.

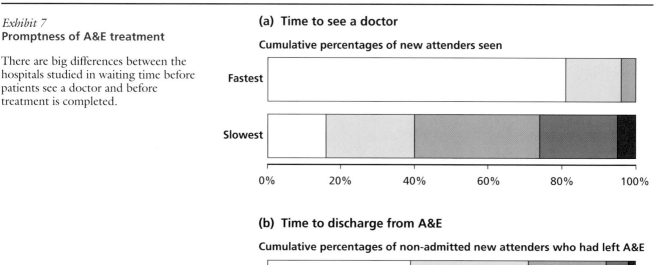

(a) Time to see a doctor

Cumulative percentages of new attenders seen

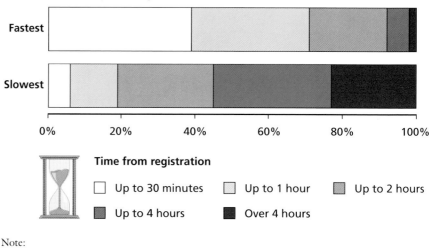

(b) Time to discharge from A&E

Cumulative percentages of non-admitted new attenders who had left A&E

Time from registration

☐ Up to 30 minutes   ☐ Up to 1 hour   ▨ Up to 2 hours

◼ Up to 4 hours   ■ Over 4 hours

Note:
Nurse practitioners are counted as doctors in this analysis if they were able to treat the patient.

Source: Audit Commission site visits

Exhibit 8

Variations in length of wait for A&E treatment at one hospital, by time of day

Waits to see a doctor can be as long in the early hours of the morning as at the busiest times of the day.

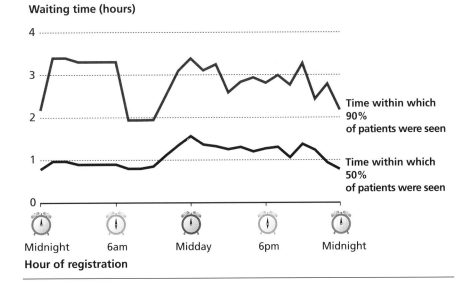

Waiting time (hours)

Time within which 90% of patients were seen

Time within which 50% of patients were seen

Midnight   6am   Midday   6pm   Midnight

Hour of registration

Source: Audit Commission site visit (6,191 patients during six one-week periods)

17. Short waits to see a doctor and for treatment to be completed cannot be guaranteed at all times because A&E departments must give priority to seriously injured patients. Nevertheless, delays in some departments are consistently longer than in others, and the reasons for this deserve exploration. Contributory factors may include:

◆ congestion;

◆ the way in which doctors and nurses are rostered;

◆ the number of doctors available; and

◆ the quality of management information, necessary for processing patients and planning.

Congestion

18. Patients referred for emergency admission to hospital need to be nursed while they are waiting in A&E. Long delays in the admission process[1] are a particular cause of congestion in many A&E departments. This congestion affects the speed with which other patients can be seen and treated and the ability of nurses to provide proper observation and care. This is one reason why, in the departments studied, the ones with the longest waits for admission also took longest to complete the treatment of other patients.

Rostering

19. Rostering A&E staff to meet demand is not easy. Even when account is taken of historic daily and seasonal patterns of attendance, there remains considerable uncertainty about how many patients will actually attend on each day, during each hour of the day (Exhibit 9, overleaf), and what resources will be needed to treat them. Often, a number of patients arrive within a short time, followed by a slack period. Even so, matching the number of doctors and nurses on duty at different times of the day to the expected workload

[1]
Waits for admission are discussed in Chapter 3, since they are largely beyond the control of the A&E department.

Exhibit 9
Variation in hourly workload in one A&E department

There is uncertainty as to how many patients will attend in any hour.

Key

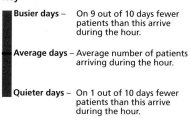

Busier days – On 9 out of 10 days fewer patients than this arrive during the hour.

Average days – Average number of patients arriving during the hour.

Quieter days – On 1 out of 10 days fewer patients than this arrive during the hour.

Source: Audit Commission site visit – arrivals during six one-week periods

Number of new A&E patients arriving during each hour

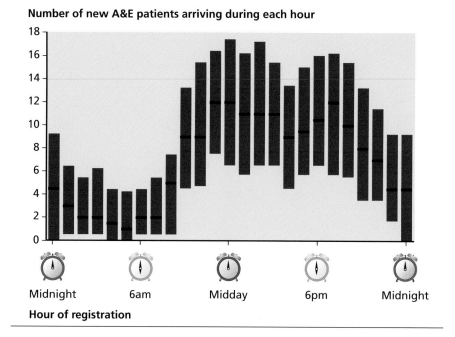

Hour of registration

could have been better at several of the departments studied:

- At one, most A&E nurses worked the same shifts as the rest of the hospital. As a result, the early shift came on duty at 7.15am, even though few patients arrived before 9am; and at the other end of the day, considerable numbers of patients were still waiting when the late shift handed over to the reduced number of nurses working nights.

- In another department, nursing shifts overlapped by three hours each afternoon.

- Some hospitals have fewer A&E doctors on duty at weekends, even though in most the number of patients is as great as on weekdays.

- A&E clinics and training sessions for junior doctors are frequently scheduled for busy times of day when delays for new attenders are generally increasing.

The number of doctors

20. It seems plausible that the time patients wait to see a doctor and for treatment is affected by the number of doctors available. It is certainly the case that some A&E departments have less than half as many doctors as others in relation to the number of patients attending. This is either because there are not enough posts, or because those that do exist cannot be filled. Although, nationally, the number of doctors in A&E departments has increased rapidly (Exhibit 10), most of the hospitals studied still have considerably fewer than the British Association for Accident & Emergency Medicine (BAEM) recommends, assuming that they work a 56-hour week (Box B, Ref. 8). Nationally, 25 per cent more senior house officers (SHOs) and 43 per cent more middle-grade doctors – costing an additional

£17 million per year – would be needed to meet BAEM targets (Exhibit 11, overleaf). Only two of the 113 hospitals surveyed had sufficient junior A&E doctors to meet the BAEM's more recent higher target based on a 40-hour week.

Exhibit 10
Medical staffing of A&E departments

Nationally, the number of doctors in A&E departments has increased rapidly.

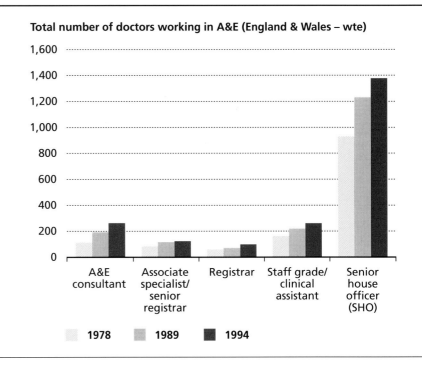

Total number of doctors working in A&E (England & Wales – wte)

Source: Department of Health (data for England and Wales)

Box B
The BAEM A&E medical staffing formulae

Because not all grades of A&E doctor can be involved equally in seeing patients, the BAEM has defined the concept of a 'SHO equivalent' doctor. This recognises that the majority of A&E patients are currently treated by SHOs. It assumes that consultants devote the majority of their time to review, audit, teaching and administration; and that for similar reasons, career middle-grade doctors are only likely to be available to see new patients for about half of their time, while registrars and senior registrars who additionally spend periods on secondment to other specialties will be available only for about 30 per cent of their time.

One 'SHO equivalent' working 40 hours per week is required for each 4,000 new patient attendances per year with a minimum of six SHOs in each department providing 24-hour cover. (This is equivalent to an *average* of 24 minutes per patient after allowance is made for annual leave and continuing medical education.) If junior doctors work a 56-hour week, then this requirement can be reduced to 1 'SHO equivalent' per 5,000 attendances, with a minimum of five.

There should be at least one 'experienced SHO', registrar, senior registrar, staff grade or associate specialist per three SHOs. An extra A&E Consultant is required for each additional 25,000 new patient attendances per year. Although consultants may see new patients when departmental pressures require it, their posts should be additional to the number of 'SHO equivalents' required.

Exhibit 11
A&E medical staffing

Most of the departments studied have fewer doctors than the BAEM recommends for a 56-hour working week. Nationally, 25 per cent more SHOs and 43 per cent more middle-grade doctors would be needed to meet the BAEM target.

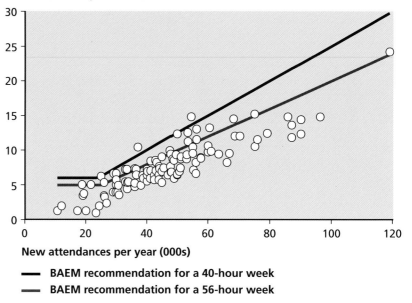

Doctors ('SHO equivalents')

New attendances per year (000s)

— **BAEM recommendation for a 40-hour week**
— **BAEM recommendation for a 56-hour week**

*Source: Audit Commission / District Audit
surveys of 113 A&E departments (1995)*

21. Part of the problem is that many A&E departments cannot attract enough doctors, particularly SHOs.[I] In February 1996, more than one in every five SHO posts was expected to be unfilled. Competition from other specialties for SHOs has increased as a result of progressive reductions in junior doctors' hours. The number of new posts alone created in other specialties within the last two years is more than half the total number of SHOs needed by A&E departments. Moreover, A&E experience is no longer a compulsory requirement for fellowship of the Royal College of Surgeons. As a result, A&E departments are increasingly having to attract non-career grade staff doctors, or rely on rotas of GPs working as clinical assistants in order to staff their departments.

22. Medical staffing at more senior grades is also inadequate at many A&E departments. Only one-quarter have the number of consultants recommended by the BAEM.[II] There is little consistency in the number of consultant posts in relation to attendances (Exhibit 12); almost 60 per cent of A&E departments have only one consultant and while some hospitals are appointing third A&E consultants, others with more patients are still seeking a second. Departments with low SHO staffing levels may have particular difficulty in attracting consultants because they will have to see new patients alongside SHOs, sometimes to the exclusion of other duties. The availability of doctors to fill A&E posts will be further affected by the faster progression through senior training grades recommended in the Calman Report (Ref. 9). It is therefore unlikely that the supply of doctors for A&E departments will be sufficient to meet demand for the foreseeable future, whether or not the funding is available.

[I]
Shortages of junior A&E doctors are particularly acute between February and July because of the sequence of postgraduate training.
[II]
It would cost an additional £12 million per year to implement BAEM recommendations for numbers of A&E consultants; the immediate constraint is the limited availability of suitable candidates to fill additional posts.

23. But employing more doctors may not in itself be sufficient to solve the problem of waiting times, whatever its effect on other aspects of quality of care: the departments studied that had more generous medical staffing did not have shorter waits for treatment (Exhibit 13). (Nor, indeed, did departments with higher reported unit costs treat patients faster.)

Exhibit 12
Number of A&E consultants

There is little consistency in the number of consultant posts in relation to attendances; while some hospitals are appointing third A&E consultants, others with more patients are still seeking a second.

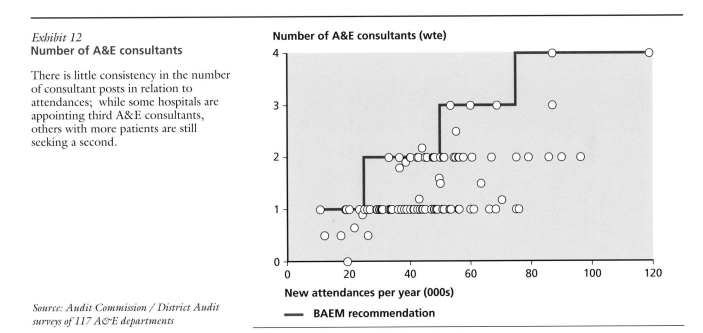

Source: Audit Commission / District Audit surveys of 117 A&E departments

Exhibit 13
Speed of treatment compared to medical staffing

The departments studied that had more generous medical staffing did not have shorter waits for treatment.

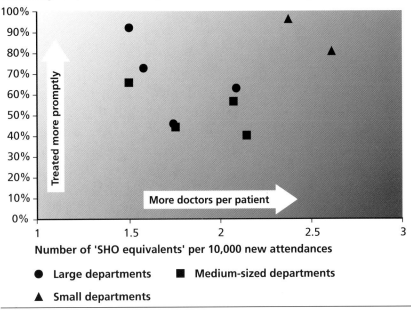

Source: Audit Commission site visits and pilot audits

'Targets should reflect real waiting times for patients.'

The average time that doctors spent on each patient during busy periods varied almost twofold between hospitals (from 13 to 22 minutes). This variation is not simply a matter of individuals' productivity. It may partly be a reflection of differences in case-mix or the quality of care provided; but other factors including supervision, departmental procedures and working practices – as well as the size and layout of the department – can also affect speed of treatment significantly.

The quality of management information

24. Weak information management and systems can affect day-to-day running and the planning of change. Both can in turn affect waiting times. Yet many departments are still operating inadequate systems, or not using them properly. A third of the A&E departments studied by the Commission still registered patients manually. Many A&E systems are inflexible and incapable of meeting the administrative, managerial and clinical needs of their departments. Some cannot exchange data with other computer systems within the hospital, resulting in duplicated and inaccurate information. There are also weaknesses in the way that more flexible systems are being used: data are often incomplete and insufficient attention is paid to data validation (Box C).

Reducing waiting times

25. The causes of long waiting times are clearly complex, and no two A&E departments will have exactly the same set of problems. But many factors are within their control. The remainder of this chapter looks at ways in which the impact of these problems could be alleviated and waiting times reduced.

Meaningful targets

26. All A&E departments should have targets which reflect real waiting times for patients and be able to monitor them accurately. In addition to the time from arrival to initial assessment, several other measures should be used:

- the time from arrival until patients are first seen by a nurse practitioner or a doctor who can *treat* them;

- the total time spent in A&E by those patients who are subsequently discharged or referred for outpatient treatment;

- the time spent in A&E by those eventually admitted for inpatient care; and

- the percentage of A&E patients who leave before treatment (which varied from 1 per cent to 8 per cent between the hospitals studied).

Targets should be agreed locally (taking account of funding implications), but comparative information on targets and their achievement should be published more widely. Comparison would be facilitated by the development of a national framework of performance indicators. This is already the practice in Scotland. Reasons for the longest waits should be audited monthly and the findings shared with purchasers.

Box C
Weaknesses in management information derived from A&E computer systems

Many A&E computer systems are inflexible or inadequate

♦ One could neither produce the cross-tabulations needed to audit whether high priority patients were being seen significantly faster than those of lower priority, nor download data to a package that could do this.

♦ At one hospital, only the hospital IT manager knew how to extract data for audit purposes.

♦ Data analysis often has to compete for limited terminal availability and processing time.

Data are often incomplete

♦ Audits at one A&E department showed that the time at which patients had first been seen by a doctor was recorded for only 66 per cent of initial attendances and it was possible to calculate the time between the decision to admit and the patient leaving A&E for only 20 per cent of relevant patients.

♦ At one hospital, the time patients left the A&E department had been recorded for only 74 per cent of attendances.

♦ Examinations and decisions made in A&E by doctors from other specialties who are unfamiliar with A&E systems are the least likely to be properly recorded.

Insufficient attention is paid to data validation

♦ Some A&E computer systems do not store a separate record of each re-attendance during an episode and overwrite certain details of that patient's initial attendance.

♦ Some computer systems automatically assume that a patient leaves A&E when the final information about the attendance is added to their A&E record; but this information is sometimes entered into the computer only when the doctor who initially treated the patient next comes back on duty.

♦ Some times are out of sequence: patients may be recorded as having first seen a doctor in A&E after they have supposedly left the department. Mistakes in using the 24-hour clock are common.

♦ Other studies have shown obvious inconsistencies between coded diagnoses and treatment and discrepancies between hospital admissions shown on the A&E computer and those recorded on the Patient Administration System (PAS).

Links between A&E computers and other hospital systems can be problematic

♦ At one hospital studied, the A&E PAS module could take up to seven minutes to produce a casualty card at times when other hospital systems were being heavily used, with consequent delays to treatment.

♦ At another, computer 'down-time' had increased markedly when the A&E system had been linked to the PAS.

27. Separate targets are needed for patients in each triage category, reflecting differences in the level of urgency of treatment required. However, these targets and data on the extent to which they are achieved will not be of much use for comparison until triage categories are standardised between hospitals. As with all indicators, such data need to be interpreted with care and should not distort individual clinical decisions. It may, for example, be best clinical practice to keep a small minority of patients (for example, those with concussion) in A&E for some hours while their condition is being monitored and, in some cases, it may be better to spend extra time on investigations before patients are seen by a doctor.

Reducing congestion

28. It is often suggested that A&E departments could reduce congestion and cut waits by controlling demand. It is certainly true that attendance rates of new patients vary markedly across the country, from less than 140 per 1,000 residents in East Anglia to over 400 per 1,000 in and around Liverpool and the inner London boroughs. A proportion of A&E patients do not require the facilities of a major hospital, but this varies considerably around the country. At Kings College Hospital, London it was judged that over 40 per cent of those attending the A&E department could have been treated equally well by a GP, if adequate 24-hour primary care had been available (Ref. 10), while at the Royal Hospital, Wolverhampton it was just 3.4 per cent (Ref. 11). However, not all of these patients are identifiable in advance of a full diagnosis. For example, triage nurses at A&E departments studied by the Audit Commission judged that between only 2 and 7 per cent of patients were suitable for primary care.

29. If some departments do have a problem of high attendance rates boosted by patients who should be receiving primary care, what can they do about it? Essentially they have two options: to turn people away or deter them from attending in the first place. Most agree that A&E departments should offer treatment to all who attend. Indeed, this may even take less time than turning people away. It is for purchasers to decide, in consultation with users, how the needs of these patients can best be met and to promote alternative facilities,[I] either in association with A&E departments or in the community.

30. On the other hand, it *is* appropriate to advise people on whether they need to attend. Many departments operate 'telephone triage' systems so that patients and carers can obtain prompt advice as to whether a trip to A&E is warranted by their condition. However, advice is often given either by hard-pressed triage nurses or by the nurse running the major treatment area. Although efforts are made to document what patients are told, records tend to be fragmented and there is little audit or specific training for nurses. Often, if there is the slightest doubt, the patient is advised to visit A&E. These services need to be made more effective (Case Study 1).

I
Possibilities are considered in
Chapter 4.

Case Study 1
Developing more effective telephone triage

Kings College Hospital is developing computer-assisted telephone triage. This decision support system, located away from the bustle of A&E department, will guide a nurse through a series of questions about a caller's symptoms, suggest possible diagnoses and the most appropriate course of action. The advice given is recorded and can be fully audited.

If this system proves successful, groups of trusts could be funded to operate telephone triage jointly. Such systems should be capable of providing information on the full spectrum of emergency care, not just A&E departments. Care should be taken to ensure that advice provided by hospital telephone triage systems is compatible with that given by computerised ambulance priority despatch systems. Consideration might be given to co-operative development and operation by hospital and ambulance trusts.

31. It may be easier to reduce the rate of planned re-attendances.[1] Nationally, re-attendance rates vary from less than 1 per cent to over 54 per cent. To some extent this reflects variation in local needs and the availability of alternative facilities, but a re-attendance rate of over 12 per cent should attract critical examination (Box D). Review is also needed if non-emergency patients are being treated in A&E clinics or receiving minor operations in A&E theatres; such attendances may get in the way of the 'core business' of A&E, which is to treat emergencies.

32. Congestion can be further reduced by ensuring that A&E patients who are likely to need relatively little medical and nursing attention do not have lengthy waits for treatment. It is already common, except in small A&E departments, for patients who are able to walk to be seen in a separately

[1]
Planned re-attendances are used, for instance, to confirm diagnoses about which junior doctors are uncertain, to monitor the quality or outcome of care provided, or for further treatment including removal of sutures and re-dressing wounds.

Box D
Ways to reduce planned A&E re-attendances

Re-attendances can be reduced by:

◆ ensuring that more patients are seen by experienced A&E doctors the first time they attend. Uncertainty by junior doctors about diagnosis or treatment can lead to more investigations and more return visits;

◆ requiring SHOs to consult a middle or senior grade doctor, if one is present in the department, before booking clinic appointments for patients;

◆ ensuring that all re-attenders are seen by a senior doctor;

◆ asking GPs to assess the quality and outcomes of treatment provided rather than arranging return A&E attendances for these to be monitored;

◆ improving knowledge of facilities offered by GP practices (eg, for removal of sutures and renewal of dressings), both through personal contact and by making a directory available;

◆ periodic audit of reasons for re-attendance to ensure that all are justified clinically or by the need to assess outcomes and the quality of care. This audit may require better information systems;

◆ agreeing protocols with other specialties for deciding who should be seen in which clinics; and

◆ discontinuing minor operations which could be performed more appropriately elsewhere.

staffed treatment area from those with more serious conditions. But even within one area, it may not always be best practice to treat A&E patients strictly in order of medical priority and time of arrival, since the care of all can be disrupted if an A&E department becomes too congested. Treating simple cases first reduces average waiting times and is unlikely to cause additional delay for patients who are more seriously ill, as it will also keep the department clear of congestion.

Matching staffing and workload better

33. A&E departments should analyse the pattern of workload and waiting times according to hour of the day and day of the week and use such information to plan doctors' and nurses' shifts. In particular, they must plan their response to peak demands as well as to average workloads. Although the precise *timing* of peaks in attendance is as unpredictable as all A&E consultants claim, their *size* and *frequency* can be forecast statistically. By quantifying this uncertainty, departments can develop contingency plans for 'opening extra checkouts' (to adopt a supermarket analogy).

34. The Edinburgh Royal Infirmary has developed a statistical model to predict and demonstrate to purchasers the effect on waiting times of increasing medical staffing at certain times of the day. Several other hospitals are experimenting with sophisticated computer simulations of patient flows through A&E to optimise the balance of resources and to show the effect of delays in other specialties and support services.

35. Such models could also be used nationally to build up credible staffing guidelines based on objective measurement as well as professional consensus. These guidelines would need to reflect local circumstances (Box E). In the meantime, the Commission's auditors will be using data on current durations of treatment during busy periods and peak arrival patterns in each A&E department to estimate the effects of marginal changes to medical staffing patterns. Numbers of doctors and nurses required to cover peaks in attendance increase rapidly as targets for maximum waiting times are reduced or interpreted more strictly.

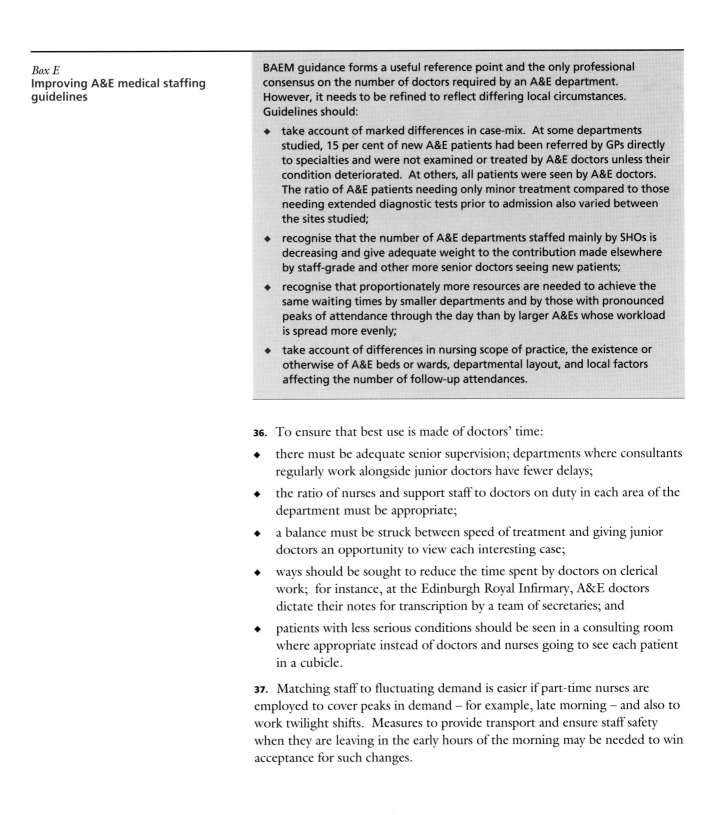

Box E
Improving A&E medical staffing guidelines

BAEM guidance forms a useful reference point and the only professional consensus on the number of doctors required by an A&E department. However, it needs to be refined to reflect differing local circumstances. Guidelines should:

◆ take account of marked differences in case-mix. At some departments studied, 15 per cent of new A&E patients had been referred by GPs directly to specialties and were not examined or treated by A&E doctors unless their condition deteriorated. At others, all patients were seen by A&E doctors. The ratio of A&E patients needing only minor treatment compared to those needing extended diagnostic tests prior to admission also varied between the sites studied;

◆ recognise that the number of A&E departments staffed mainly by SHOs is decreasing and give adequate weight to the contribution made elsewhere by staff-grade and other more senior doctors seeing new patients;

◆ recognise that proportionately more resources are needed to achieve the same waiting times by smaller departments and by those with pronounced peaks of attendance through the day than by larger A&Es whose workload is spread more evenly;

◆ take account of differences in nursing scope of practice, the existence or otherwise of A&E beds or wards, departmental layout, and local factors affecting the number of follow-up attendances.

36. To ensure that best use is made of doctors' time:

◆ there must be adequate senior supervision; departments where consultants regularly work alongside junior doctors have fewer delays;

◆ the ratio of nurses and support staff to doctors on duty in each area of the department must be appropriate;

◆ a balance must be struck between speed of treatment and giving junior doctors an opportunity to view each interesting case;

◆ ways should be sought to reduce the time spent by doctors on clerical work; for instance, at the Edinburgh Royal Infirmary, A&E doctors dictate their notes for transcription by a team of secretaries; and

◆ patients with less serious conditions should be seen in a consulting room where appropriate instead of doctors and nurses going to see each patient in a cubicle.

37. Matching staff to fluctuating demand is easier if part-time nurses are employed to cover peaks in demand – for example, late morning – and also to work twilight shifts. Measures to provide transport and ensure staff safety when they are leaving in the early hours of the morning may be needed to win acceptance for such changes.

'Expanding the scope of nursing practice gives added flexibility, eases pressures on doctors and speeds up the flow of patients.'

Alternative ways of coping with the demand

38. There is considerable variation between hospitals in what A&E nurses do. Given the current difficulty in recruiting enough doctors to treat all patients within acceptable times, there is a strong case for *revising the scope of nursing practice*. At some hospitals A&E nurses have been trained to suture wounds, take blood samples, apply plaster of Paris, and to undertake ECGs, defibrillation and gastric lavage. This added flexibility helps to speed up patient flows as well as easing pressures on medical staff. The Edinburgh Royal Infirmary found that if routine X-rays were requested by a nurse during initial assessment, the total time that patients spent in the department was reduced by an average of 30 minutes. Similar schemes were in operation at five of the eleven hospitals studied.

39. Almost one-third of A&E departments have gone even further than the developments outlined above by training *emergency nurse practitioners*.[1] These nurses are authorised to diagnose, treat and discharge or refer patients without reference to a doctor, using agreed protocols. At Southend, one-quarter of all A&E patients are treated solely by nurses, and most are discharged within 15 minutes of arrival. They are given the option of waiting to see a doctor if they wish. Assistants trained to NVQ level 3 have also been introduced to help the nurse practitioners and to carry out simple dressings under their direction.

40. Nurse practitioners are not necessarily cheaper than doctors. It costs about 25 per cent more per hour to employ a 'G grade' nurse than a SHO. The added cost may be outweighed by improved continuity of patient care, the nurse's accumulated expertise and speed in undertaking a range of procedures, and reduced delays in treatment. However, a better quality of care will be assured only if nurse practitioners are given adequate training, well thought-out protocols agreed by all relevant specialties and access to advice from senior doctors, and if their work is regularly audited (Box F). This has not always been the case. A study in 1991 (Ref. 12) found that many nurses were acting in this role 'unofficially', without specific training or protocols.

1
The growing role of nurse practitioners in minor injuries units is discussed in Chapter 4.

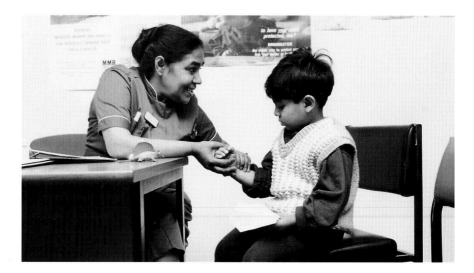

Box F
More effective use of emergency nurse practitioners

◆ **Better training**

There should be courses specifically for nurse practitioners working in A&E departments with a common core content and accredited by the English and Welsh National Boards.

◆ **Appropriate scope of practice**

Expanded nursing roles must reflect local circumstances and the frequency with which nurses would be called upon to use each skill. Protocols both for what nurse practitioners are allowed to do, and to whom, must be developed and agreed locally, but comparative information on current practice and specimen protocols should be made available to guide these local decisions. (There are currently wide differences. Some nurse practitioners, for instance, are allowed to treat children aged over 12 months; at other hospitals the minimum age is 5 years.)

◆ **Access to senior medical advice**

Experienced nurse practitioners should have the same access to senior medical advice as A&E doctors and should not be supervised by junior doctors.

◆ **Regular audit**

There should be regular interdisciplinary audit of nurse practitioner activity and its documentation, including reasons why relevant patients are referred on to a doctor.

◆ **Maintaining competence**

All nurse practitioners need to rotate to other roles to avoid losing their broader skills. The frequency with which they use each of their practitioner competencies should also be monitored.

◆ **Interpreting X-rays**

All nurse practitioners should be able to *request* certain types of X-rays. There are now moves in some A&E departments to authorise them also to *interpret* these X-rays and, if their protocols allow, to treat patients accordingly. A trial at Southend found that, after nine hours' training, both nurse practitioners and radiographers were more expert than junior doctors in reading relevant X-rays. In consequence, nurse practitioners at this hospital are now permitted after training to interpret the X-rays they request. This eliminates the duplicated work which occurs where a doctor has to take a patient's medical history again in order to interpret an X-ray requested by a nurse.

◆ **Nurse dispensing**

Consideration should also be given to empowering nurse practitioners in A&E departments to dispense a limited number of drugs, including certain painkillers, without seeking the specific authority of a doctor. This could reduce delays considerably and provide more timely patient care.

41. There is a limit to the extent to which nurse practitioners can compensate for inadequate numbers of junior doctors, since they cannot be deployed so flexibly to treat patients with differing clinical needs. This limit will be determined by each department's case-mix.

42. Changes to the scope of nursing practice must be accompanied by a review of staffing levels. Numbers of nurses currently vary widely in relation to attendances (Exhibit 14) and also to numbers of doctors. This variation is greater than can be explained by differences in scope of practice or departmental layout. Nurse practitioners should have a distinct role within an A&E department, although it is advisable that they rotate to other duties from time to time so as to maintain their full range of skills. Hospitals should ensure that they have enough A&E nurses to undertake traditional nursing duties before introducing nurse practitioners. If not, either basic nursing care will be neglected, or, as has happened at some hospitals, nurse practitioners will frequently find themselves having to revert from their enhanced role to care for other patients. If nurse practitioners would be unable to treat enough patients independently to justify their higher cost or to maintain their clinical competencies, lesser extensions to the scope of nursing practice may represent better value for money.

Improving initial assessment

43. However well a department is staffed, there will always be circumstances in which some patients have to wait. The Patient's Charter has been valuable in promoting initial assessment, which is vital to ensure that those who need

Exhibit 14
A&E nurse staffing

Numbers of nurses vary widely in relation to attendances.

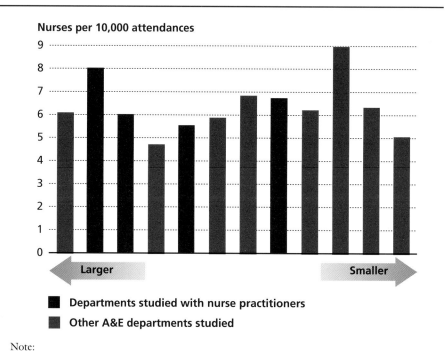

Nurses per 10,000 attendances

■ **Departments studied with nurse practitioners**
■ **Other A&E departments studied**

Source: Audit Commission site visits and pilot audits

Note:
Nurses staffing A&E observation or admission wards have been excluded.

'Initial assessment can take between 10 and 15 per cent of A&E nursing resources, so must be done well.'

urgent treatment are seen rapidly, particularly if they have symptoms of uncertain significance such as chest pain. However, 24-hour initial assessment costs each department a minimum of £90,000 per year, or between 10 and 15 per cent of the total nursing budget of a medium-sized A&E department. It is therefore essential that it is done well. Good initial assessment can speed up the treatment of all patients, not just those who are given priority, because of better overall planning. Moreover, by keeping patients informed and allaying their anxiety, it can make waiting more acceptable.

44. In order to achieve this, patients should ideally be:

♦ given first aid if this is needed, to relieve both their own anxiety and that of other patients in the waiting room;

♦ relieved of acute pain, if this can be done without affecting subsequent diagnosis;

♦ reassured, where appropriate, that their condition is stable and that there is a nurse keeping an eye on them in case it deteriorates;

♦ told where they will have to go in the department, what treatment to expect, how long they are likely to wait, and how this delay could be affected if a seriously injured patient is brought in; and

♦ kept informed periodically of where they are in the queue and of any subsequent delays.

Triage nurses should then:

♦ request any relevant X-rays or tests not requiring prior examination by a doctor;

♦ ensure that responsibility for the patient's further care is handed over to a named nurse; and

♦ keep the nurse in charge of the department informed of the numbers of patients waiting and of their likely requirements for treatment.

45. In practice, the way initial assessment is being conducted often falls short of these ideals. For example, in some A&E departments:

♦ there is an element of wasteful duplication, especially at times when there is no wait to see a doctor, and also in those departments where a brief initial assessment by a nurse is followed, after registration, by fuller triage;

♦ patients can become confused by the rules and, unless clearly informed, may not understand that the Patient's Charter guarantees assessment and not treatment within five minutes of arrival;

♦ there is often little privacy for patients asked to reveal intimate details while they are being assessed;

♦ training and audit may be insufficient to ensure that the triage criteria used by nurses during initial assessment are applied consistently (Exhibit 15, overleaf); and

♦ the whole process is surrounded by the collection of inconsistent and dubious statistics.

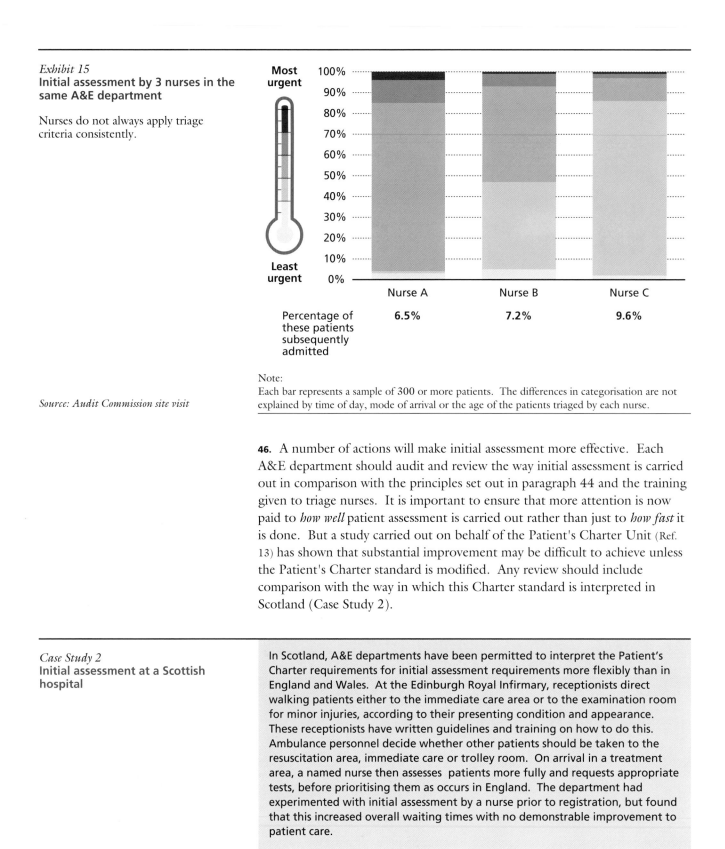

Exhibit 15
Initial assessment by 3 nurses in the same A&E department

Nurses do not always apply triage criteria consistently.

Most urgent

Least urgent

	Nurse A	Nurse B	Nurse C
Percentage of these patients subsequently admitted	6.5%	7.2%	9.6%

Source: Audit Commission site visit

Note:
Each bar represents a sample of 300 or more patients. The differences in categorisation are not explained by time of day, mode of arrival or the age of the patients triaged by each nurse.

46. A number of actions will make initial assessment more effective. Each A&E department should audit and review the way initial assessment is carried out in comparison with the principles set out in paragraph 44 and the training given to triage nurses. It is important to ensure that more attention is now paid to *how well* patient assessment is carried out rather than just to *how fast* it is done. But a study carried out on behalf of the Patient's Charter Unit (Ref. 13) has shown that substantial improvement may be difficult to achieve unless the Patient's Charter standard is modified. Any review should include comparison with the way in which this Charter standard is interpreted in Scotland (Case Study 2).

Case Study 2
Initial assessment at a Scottish hospital

In Scotland, A&E departments have been permitted to interpret the Patient's Charter requirements for initial assessment requirements more flexibly than in England and Wales. At the Edinburgh Royal Infirmary, receptionists direct walking patients either to the immediate care area or to the examination room for minor injuries, according to their presenting condition and appearance. These receptionists have written guidelines and training on how to do this. Ambulance personnel decide whether other patients should be taken to the resuscitation area, immediate care or trolley room. On arrival in a treatment area, a named nurse then assesses patients more fully and requests appropriate tests, before prioritising them as occurs in England. The department had experimented with initial assessment by a nurse prior to registration, but found that this increased overall waiting times with no demonstrable improvement to patient care.

'Better and more complete recording of information should be a priority to improve departmental management and clinical care.'

47. Standardising triage categories nationally will facilitate nurse training and meaningful comparison of hospitals' A&E case-mix, waiting time targets and achievement. The BAEM is currently considering whether standard triage categories based on objective criteria could be introduced throughout Britain. This has been done in Australia where it has not only been beneficial for patients but has also prompted the development of a new A&E case-mix costing system based partly on assessed urgency of treatment.

Better availability and use of management information

48. Better and more complete recording of clinical information and the times of each key stage of treatment must be a first priority. Doctors, nurses and support services must be given both the incentive and the resources to do this accurately (Box G). Incentives should be reinforced by audit. The virtues of

Box G
Improving data for audit and management

♦ **Incentives to record data**

Following registration, data are either entered on to the computer as patients proceed through the department, or are recorded manually and subsequently keyed in by clerical staff. The former is more time-consuming for clinical staff but offers greater incentives to record data accurately. These incentives include quicker and easier production of X-ray requests and GP discharge letters, and easier patient location. Responsibility for entering information should rest with whichever staff have the greatest operational use for it. Nurses, for example, should record the times that patients go to and return from X-ray or when specialty doctors attend, since they are most affected by uncertainty over the status of a patient and by lengthy trolley waits. Some A&E departments use barcodes on patient documentation to make it easier for nurses to register the start of each key stage of treatment on the computer.

♦ **Maximising the use of data**

Flexible reporting facilities are required that are capable of performing cross-tabulations of several datafields. It should be possible to select and download attendance data fulfilling specified conditions for clinical audit purposes.

♦ **System reliability**

A&E systems need to be fully operational for 24 hours a day, 365 days a year. Links between A&E and other hospital clinical and administrative systems can be highly advantageous, but it is vital that overloading or faults in network linkages do not cause the A&E system to fail.

♦ **Allowing for the effects of varying A&E case-mix**

The National Casemix Office has recently published a 'Case-mix Grouper' for A&E based on how patients leave the department; in particular, whether or not they are admitted for inpatient treatment. Preliminary indications are that admitted patients typically use 2.2 times as many A&E resources as do discharged patients. Hospitals in Western Australia have developed a new A&E case-mix costing system based, inter-alia, on urgency of treatment. This has been shown to be a significant factor in determining resource utilisation. The Royal Infirmary, Edinburgh has adapted this methodology to calculate the differing resource requirements of patients in each area of its A&E department. Greater standardisation of priority categories will be required if this method is to be used to compare the case-mix of different hospitals.

computerisation are clear in an environment as complex as an A&E department. However, the A&E system must be sufficiently flexible to produce useful information for clinical audit as well as management.

————————

49. This chapter has looked in depth at waiting times, since these are top of most people's list of A&E issues. However, although waiting time is important, it is far from being the only factor that matters to patients. Chapter 2 looks at a number of other issues that determine the quality of emergency care, including the way A&E departments interface with GPs and community services.

Recommendations

The Department of Health and the Welsh Office should:

1 establish a framework of performance measures for all A&E departments which reflect real waiting times for patients (Para. 26);

2 publish local waiting time targets and performance against them (Para. 26);

3 standardise triage categories to facilitate comparison of waiting times and case-mix (Para. 27);

4 with the BAEM, refine A&E staffing guidelines to take account of local circumstances (Para. 35); and

5 modify the Patient's Charter initial assessment requirements to make initial assessment more effective (Para. 46).

Health commissioning bodies should:

6 set and monitor realistic, measurable targets for A&E waiting times (Para. 26), taking account of any funding implications; and

7 look for alternative ways to meet the needs of A&E patients who require primary care (Paras. 29, 30).

Acute hospital trusts with A&E departments should:

Information

8 monitor real A&E waiting times for patients against locally agreed targets (Para. 26);

9 provide advice and information to help patients decide whether A&E attendance is necessary (Para. 30);

10   analyse patterns of A&E workload and delays and use information to adjust resource scheduling to match demand (Para. 33);

11   promote better recording of clinical information and times of key treatment stages (Para. 48); and

12   find ways to make more flexible use of information for clinical audit and management (Para. 48).

Staffing

13   look for opportunities to expand the scope of nursing practice in A&E and to introduce emergency nurse practitioners, making any necessary changes to staffing levels and training (Paras. 38-42).

Procedures

14   critically examine A&E re-attendance rates higher than 12 per cent (Para. 31);

15   establish procedures to enable simple cases to be treated and discharged quickly (Para. 32);

16   enable emergency nurse practitioners and experienced triage nurses to request certain X-rays and diagnostic tests, subject to audit (Paras. 38, 44);

17   improve initial assessment to provide patients with information, assurance and first aid, as well as a priority category (Paras. 44-46); and

18   increase the consistency of triage through training and audit (Para. 46).

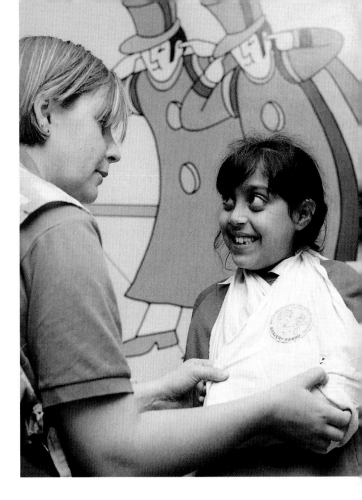

2 Minding the Quality

A&E treatment must be both professionally competent and sympathetic. Clinical competence should be promoted through an increased senior medical presence, audit and training.

Some patients need continuing care after they leave A&E – good communication with GPs and community services is vital.

Increased awareness of the special needs of children, psychologically disturbed patients, the bereaved and other potentially vulnerable people using A&E departments is also required.

Hospitals need to find out what patients thought about specific aspects of their A&E treatment and use this information to improve quality of care.

50. The way patients are treated in A&E departments is as important to them as not being kept waiting. A number of the former NHS regions produced guidelines on applicable quality standards (Refs. 14-16), and the NHS Executive has suggested indicators of an effective, user-friendly A&E service (Appendix 5). This chapter considers four aspects of quality care:

◆ above all, patients want to be sure that they will receive appropriate care from doctors and nurses who are clinically competent;

◆ the care of some who attend A&E will need to be continued after discharge, so good communication with GPs and community services as well as with patients is vital;

◆ a visit to an A&E department is likely to be particularly traumatic for some groups of patients; their experience illustrates the importance of sympathetic care by appropriately trained staff in a suitable environment; and

◆ hospitals also need to ensure that they have effective mechanisms for finding out how patients felt about their treatment and using this information to improve quality of care.

Developing clinical competence

51. An expert panel appointed by the British Orthopaedic Association in 1992 estimated that 20 per cent of patients treated for orthopaedic injuries had been left with some degree of disability which could have been prevented (Ref. 17, Exhibit 16). This was attributed both to misdiagnosis and to technical errors in treatment due to inadequate training, insufficient specialist interest in trauma and lack of supervision of junior doctors. While many of these issues relate to specialist orthopaedic care, there are similar concerns about A&E departments which provide initial diagnosis and treatment for these injuries. It is therefore essential to ensure that clinical competence is developed, both through expert guidance, supervision and systems of feedback and clinical audit.

Exhibit 16
Disability following care for orthopaedic trauma

The British Orthopaedic Association estimated that 20 per cent of patients treated for orthopaedic injuries had been left with some preventable disability.

Source: British Orthopaedic Association Trauma Audit (expert assessment of 800 patients)

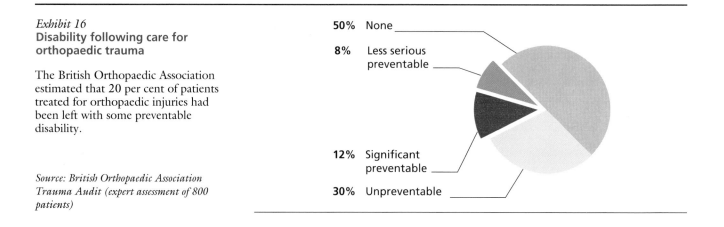

50% None

8% Less serious preventable

12% Significant preventable

30% Unpreventable

Guidance and supervision

52. Most A&E patients are treated by SHOs, many of whom are relatively inexperienced. Senior doctors in hard-pressed departments seldom have sufficient time for effective supervision, informal teaching and management. There is also marked variation between hospitals in the number of hours per week that a senior or middle-grade A&E doctor is present on site, independent of the size of the department (Exhibit 17). Even some quite busy A&E departments are staffed outside the normal working week by SHOs alone, despite the fact that almost 60 per cent of new attenders (and 70 per cent of '999' patients) arrive at these times.

53. It is generally acknowledged that new, inexperienced SHOs should not work at night without support. Ideally there should be a senior or middle-grade A&E doctor in all A&E departments for at least 15 hours a day, 7 days a week (112 hours) and a middle-grade on call within the hospital for the remaining time.

54. The level of funding of middle-grade posts should be sufficient to ensure that cover does not lapse when registrars are on secondment to other specialties. Departments which are unable to obtain registrar cover may find it possible to recruit A&E staff-grade (or equivalent) doctors – perhaps part-time – on short-term renewable contracts with provision for continuing training. Alternatively, it may be necessary to supplement A&E SHO cover at night with advice from on-call middle-grade doctors in other specialties.

Exhibit 17
Experienced medical cover in A&E

There is marked variation in the number of hours per week that a senior or middle-grade A&E doctor is present on site.

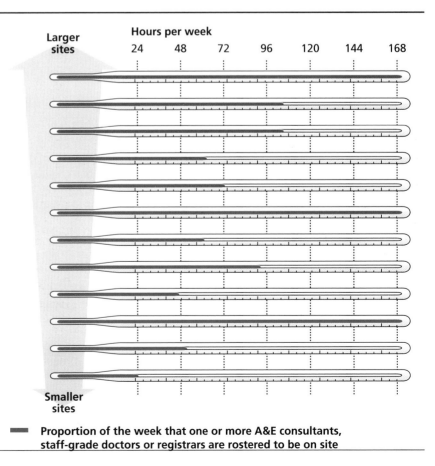

Larger sites

Hours per week

| 24 | 48 | 72 | 96 | 120 | 144 | 168 |

Smaller sites

▬ **Proportion of the week that one or more A&E consultants, staff-grade doctors or registrars are rostered to be on site**

Source: Audit Commission site visits

55. All A&E departments should have rules for when to inform the on-call consultant about clinically complex cases, and also when waiting times exceed agreed limits. SHOs are more likely to seek help if they do not have to disturb a consultant at home. Where practical, A&E departments should establish 'out-of-hours' arrangements with neighbouring trusts, whereby a senior doctor resident at one hospital is available on call should junior doctors at the other hospitals require advice or assistance. Such arrangements work best if the departments involved work together at other times, with shared teaching and audit sessions and common protocols.

Clinical audit and feedback

56. Regular clinical audit and feedback are essential for all clinical staff. Most A&E departments studied audited the processes of care regularly, including documentation and the use and interpretation of X-rays (Case Study 3). Audits of the treatment of patients with specific presenting conditions or diagnoses, such as acute chest pain, were also widely undertaken. However, three major shortcomings emerged. First, patients who go on to be admitted spend relatively little time in A&E and it is hard to assess the outcome of their A&E care in isolation. Many audits therefore need to be inter-specialty and, where appropriate, should also involve ambulance services and others providing pre-hospital care. Yet at the hospitals studied, the audit process tended to stop at the point where responsibility for a patient passed to another specialty. Secondly, only a minority of A&E departments undertake true clinical audit embracing nursing as well as medical care provided to patients. Thirdly, although many A&E departments now participate in the national Major Trauma Outcome Study, there is considerable scope for more inter-hospital audit and external review.

Case Study 3
A&E audit & feedback (1)

At Southend, A&E audit concentrates on picking up non-compliance with standards and protocols:

♦ monthly medical and clinical audit: one card in every hundred is audited either by one of the consultants or by the nurse/business manager; (this kind of multidisciplinary audit – a nurse auditing doctors – is very rare);

♦ the work of nurse practitioners is audited in the same way as that of doctors;

♦ the consultant and senior doctors audit all X-ray requests and give monthly feedback to SHOs – eg, on false negatives/positives and incorrect diagnoses; in consequence, SHOs are less likely to request investigations which will not materially affect the way a patient is treated;

♦ deaths are audited monthly and the A&E department also co-ordinates an inter-specialty audit of cardiac arrest results; and

♦ topic-based audits have included paediatric attendances and paediatricians' response times, care of elderly patients, fractured neck of femur, trolley waits, ambulance service transport response and X-ray requests. One is carried out by each SHO. Topics are increasingly audited concurrently by a number of A&E departments, assisted by a regional A&E medical audit co-ordinator, so that findings can be compared and common lessons learnt.

Case Study 4 A&E audit & feedback (2)	The West Cumbria Hospital has a small A&E department with a single consultant. The consultant reviews a sample of CAS cards (A&E records) each morning and picks out interesting features or examples where protocols have not been followed. He or she writes these on a feedback board with a rating of their importance.
	There is good liaison between specialties and A&E. There are weekly meetings attended by all radiologists, the senior radiographer, three orthopaedic consultants, general surgical HOs, the A&E consultant and any free SHOs. These were instigated because surgeons were picking up problems that they felt could have been better managed in the A&E department, and because A&E doctors received little feedback on patients referred to specialties. The radiologists also wanted more feedback – for example, were trauma foreign bodies being missed? They discuss such matters as post-operative follow-up, what types of dislocations should be manipulated by A&E doctors, and which patients require more than one X-ray view.
	All SHOs are also asked to carry out a formal audit during their time with the department. Topics have included thrombolysis, primary care in A&E, unscheduled re-attenders. Every fourth month, A&E presents to the surgical audit forum. In addition the trauma team has a joint audit meeting at which all trauma team cases are reviewed. General Medicine audits cardiac arrest monthly and there has been a hospital-wide audit of acute myocardial infarction.
	The Director of Nursing Practice has also introduced a standard quality assessment procedure applicable to all disciplines throughout the hospital. This includes self-assessment tools for training, standards, performance reviews at all levels and investment in quality initiatives.

57. Not all feedback requires formal, retrospective audit. A balance needs to be drawn between this and more active supervision of clinical work. For example, it may be more productive to provide feedback to junior doctors while cases are still clear in their minds. At the Edinburgh Royal Infirmary, two 15-minute periods each day are reserved for this, and at the West Cumbria Hospital a feedback board is used (Case Study 4).

Discharge from A&E

58. The majority of patients treated in A&E departments are discharged home or into the care of their GP. Appropriate follow-up care requires good communication between A&E departments and GPs, clear instructions for the patient and mechanisms for identifying frail patients who may require additional community or social services after discharge.

Communicating with GPs

59. GPs bear a legal responsibility for providing any follow-up treatment or medication that their patients may require after discharge from A&E. They therefore need to be informed reliably and promptly whenever somebody on their list attends an A&E department. GPs should be notified even if no further care is needed, since this helps them to assess the health needs of their practice populations and to try to ensure that patients do not seek hospital treatment for conditions which could have been treated more effectively in GPs' own surgeries. However, GPs do not always receive such notification and when they do it may be in a format which is difficult for them to use.

'The accuracy, timeliness and usefulness of the information sent to GPs when a patient is discharged from A&E should be audited and improved.'

60. Traditionally, GP notification, if any, has been by a carbon copy of the A&E notes. There can be long delays in completing these notes and dispatching the copy and it can be difficult for GPs to find relevant details. Some A&E departments give a letter for the GP to patients as they leave. Some of these letters never arrive; others are received much later when the patient requests repeat medication.

61. Many A&E computer systems produce a GP letter or notification card automatically, as a by-product of operational systems. However, there can still be delays. For example, some systems will only produce a letter once all the information about that patient's diagnosis, test results, procedures and destination has been entered. Miscoding of diagnoses or procedures by rushed doctors can result in the dispatch of misleading or meaningless letters.

62. The accuracy, timeliness and usefulness of the information sent to GPs should be audited and improved. Comparatively minor changes to GP letters can make a big difference to whether the information is acted upon. Hull Royal Infirmary, for example, cut out unnecessary detail from their GP notifications and changed the format so that they could be inserted more easily into patient notes. At the Prince Philip Hospital, Llanelli, all computer-generated letters are checked to ensure that they are clinically consistent and that any miscoded data are corrected.

Information for patients

63. Sometimes patients are asked to undertake exercises or monitor their own condition after discharge from A&E. Many hospitals have therefore developed printed discharge instructions for the follow-up and self-care of various conditions. Patients may also need to know who to contact if they have further questions or worries. Southend Hospital uses computer-generated, personalised patient discharge instructions (Case Study 5) to improve the impact of this information and to reduce the number of pieces of paper given to patients on discharge. The patient is required to sign a copy which is filed in the A&E notes lest there be any future query or dispute about what the patient was told. Surveys have shown these personalised instructions to be popular with patients.

Case Study 5
An example of personalised patient discharge instructions

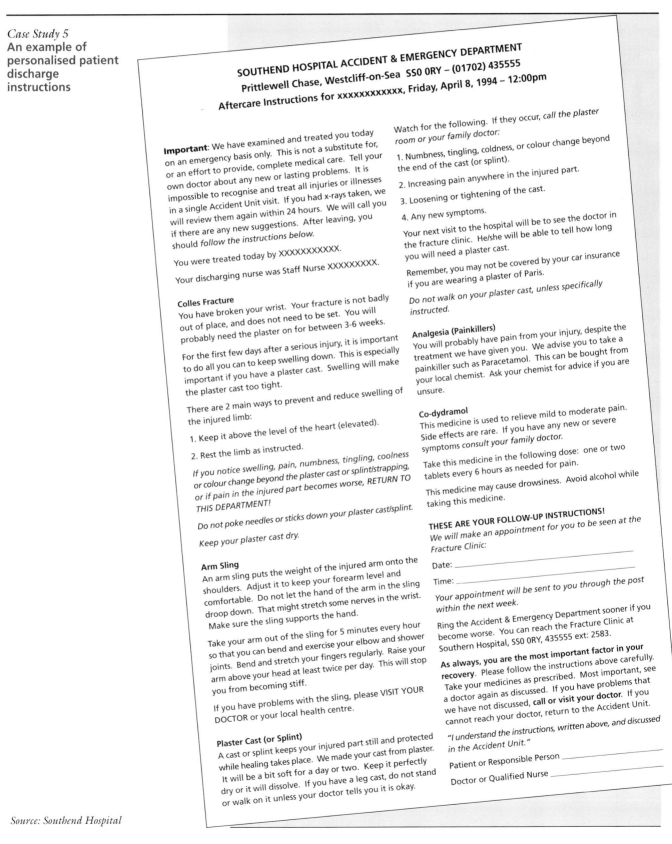

SOUTHEND HOSPITAL ACCIDENT & EMERGENCY DEPARTMENT
Prittlewell Chase, Westcliff-on-Sea SS0 0RY – (01702) 435555
Aftercare Instructions for xxxxxxxxxxxx, Friday, April 8, 1994 – 12:00pm

Important: We have examined and treated you today on an emergency basis only. This is not a substitute for, or an effort to provide, complete medical care. Tell your own doctor about any new or lasting problems. It is impossible to recognise and treat all injuries or illnesses in a single Accident Unit visit. If you had x-rays taken, we will review them again within 24 hours. We will call you if there are any new suggestions. After leaving, you should *follow the instructions below.*

You were treated today by XXXXXXXXXXXX.

Your discharging nurse was Staff Nurse XXXXXXXXX.

Colles Fracture
You have broken your wrist. Your fracture is not badly out of place, and does not need to be set. You will probably need the plaster on for between 3-6 weeks.

For the first few days after a serious injury, it is important to do all you can to keep swelling down. This is especially important if you have a plaster cast. Swelling will make the plaster cast too tight.

There are 2 main ways to prevent and reduce swelling of the injured limb:

1. Keep it above the level of the heart (elevated).

2. Rest the limb as instructed.

If you notice swelling, pain, numbness, tingling, coolness or colour change beyond the plaster cast or splint/strapping, or if pain in the injured part becomes worse, RETURN TO THIS DEPARTMENT!

Do not poke needles or sticks down your plaster cast/splint.

Keep your plaster cast dry.

Arm Sling
An arm sling puts the weight of the injured arm onto the shoulders. Adjust it to keep your forearm level and comfortable. Do not let the hand of the arm in the sling droop down. That might stretch some nerves in the wrist. Make sure the sling supports the hand.

Take your arm out of the sling for 5 minutes every hour so that you can bend and exercise your elbow and shower joints. Bend and stretch your fingers regularly. Raise your arm above your head at least twice per day. This will stop you from becoming stiff.

If you have problems with the sling, please VISIT YOUR DOCTOR or your local health centre.

Plaster Cast (or Splint)
A cast or splint keeps your injured part still and protected while healing takes place. We made your cast from plaster. It will be a bit soft for a day or two. Keep it perfectly dry or it will dissolve. If you have a leg cast, do not stand or walk on it unless your doctor tells you it is okay.

Watch for the following. If they occur, *call the plaster room or your family doctor:*

1. Numbness, tingling, coldness, or colour change beyond the end of the cast (or splint).

2. Increasing pain anywhere in the injured part.

3. Loosening or tightening of the cast.

4. Any new symptoms.

Your next visit to the hospital will be to see the doctor in the fracture clinic. He/she will be able to tell how long you will need a plaster cast.

Remember, you may not be covered by your car insurance if you are wearing a plaster of Paris.

Do not walk on your plaster cast, unless specifically instructed.

Analgesia (Painkillers)
You will probably have pain from your injury, despite the treatment we have given you. We advise you to take a painkiller such as Paracetamol. This can be bought from your local chemist. Ask your chemist for advice if you are unsure.

Co-dydramol
This medicine is used to relieve mild to moderate pain. Side effects are rare. If you have any new or severe symptoms *consult your family doctor.*

Take this medicine in the following dose: one or two tablets every 6 hours as needed for pain.

This medicine may cause drowsiness. Avoid alcohol while taking this medicine.

THESE ARE YOUR FOLLOW-UP INSTRUCTIONS!
We will make an appointment for you to be seen at the Fracture Clinic:

Date: _____

Time: _____
Your appointment will be sent to you through the post within the next week.

Ring the Accident & Emergency Department sooner if you become worse. You can reach the Fracture Clinic at Southern Hospital, SS0 0RY, 435555 ext: 2583.

As always, you are the most important factor in your recovery. Please follow the instructions above carefully. Take your medicines as prescribed. Most important, see a doctor again as discussed. If you have problems that we have not discussed, **call or visit your doctor**. If you cannot reach your doctor, return to the Accident Unit.

"I understand the instructions, written above, and discussed in the Accident Unit."

Patient or Responsible Person _____

Doctor or Qualified Nurse _____

Source: Southend Hospital

Case Study 6
Following up frail patients
discharged from A&E

St Mary's, Paddington employs an occupational therapist (OT) as part of its A&E team. Her job is to ensure that patients do not have problems managing at home after discharge from A&E or the admissions ward in order to minimise inappropriate hospital admissions for social reasons and avoidable re-admissions. A&E doctors and nurses use a form to screen all patients aged 65 years and over for factors which could cause a crisis and precipitate further attendance. If there is doubt, the OT assesses the patient in A&E. Every patient seen by the OT is followed up with a home visit or telephone call within two days. She or he also provides an interface between social services and hospital care by arranging home helps, home care, housing benefit, or referral to a community agency. This helps to reduce pressure on the A&E nursing and medical staff.

Following up the care of frail elderly patients

64. Frail elderly patients often assure doctors and nurses that they will be able to manage at home, in order to get out of hospital as quickly as possible. But appearances can be deceptive. An elderly patient who has fallen, for example, may appear to walk well in A&E but have stiffened up by the next morning. It is therefore important to check on old people discharged directly from A&E, particularly if they live alone. However, at 30 per cent of A&E departments visited there was no follow-up of elderly patients discharged directly home. Others, in contrast, are developing protocols and checklists for A&E staff to use when deciding if a referral is necessary. Some have attached community liaison health visitors, nurses or occupational therapists who make follow-up visits or telephone checks (Case Study 6). One experimental scheme offers home safety checks to all elderly patients who attend A&E after accidents in their homes.

The experience of potentially vulnerable patients

65. A visit to A&E can be particularly distressing for some potentially vulnerable patients. A recent Audit Commission report examined the hospital experience of one such group of patients, the frail elderly (Ref. 18, Appendix 6). This section illustrates quality of A&E care by focusing on three other vulnerable groups: children, people who are psychologically disturbed, and the bereaved.

Caring for children in A&E

66. For many children, a visit to A&E is their first contact with a hospital since birth. Nationally, one-quarter of all A&E patients are aged under 16. Over 98 per cent attend general A&E departments. (The eight specialist children's A&E units are beyond the scope of this report, as are walk-in paediatric clinics which deal only with medical emergencies). The Audit Commission report, *Children First* (Ref. 19), identified five key principles which should govern all aspects of the care of sick children in hospital:

◆ effective treatment;

◆ child- and family-centred care;

◆ specially skilled staff;

◆ separate facilities; and

◆ appropriate hospitalisation.

Each of these is relevant to A&E treatment (Appendix 7). A&E staff also need always to bear in mind the possibility that some injuries to children might not be accidental.

67. A&E doctors and nurses treating sick or injured children need additional skills, including different observation techniques and psychological support skills, familiarity with childhood diseases and appropriate drug doses, and an ability to involve parents in the care of the child (Ref. 20). The Department of Health set a target standard in 1991 (Ref. 21) that each A&E department which treats children should have at least one Registered Sick Children's Nurse (RSCN)[1] on duty 24 hours a day. None of the A&E departments studied came close to meeting this standard. A national shortage of RSCNs with appropriate experience makes it difficult to achieve the standard in the short term, but each A&E department should, as a minimum, have at least one child-trained nurse with sufficient seniority to take a lead in raising awareness of children's issues.

68. Specialist medical expertise is equally essential for treating children well. The Clinical Standards Advisory Group has stated that every hospital with an A&E department should have on-site paediatricians. Many do not, and the compensatory arrangements made with other hospitals or community services are not always adequate.

69. The National Association for the Welfare of Children and Young People in Hospital recommended in 1984 that all A&E departments treating children should have suitably equipped waiting and treatment areas separate from those used by adults (Ref. 22), and this has now been proposed as a requirement of the forthcoming Children's Charter. But a recent Audit Commission survey found that although most A&E departments have a separate treatment room for children, less than half have a separate waiting area (Exhibit 18). And, even where there are separate children's areas, they are not always open when needed or well used (Box H, overleaf).

[1]
A nurse who has completed the 'Child Branch' of Project 2000 is an alternative.

Exhibit 18
Separate facilities for children in A&E departments

82 per cent of A&E departments have a separate treatment room for children, but only 48 per cent have a separate waiting area.

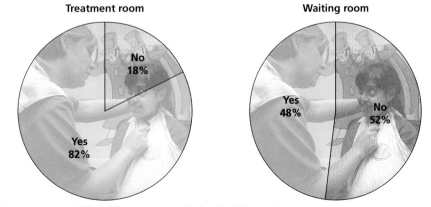

Treatment room

Waiting room

Note: Sample sizes: 80 (treatment area); 77 (waiting room) – excludes 'don't knows'

Source: Audit Commission survey (hospitals without separate children's A&E departments)

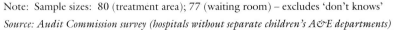

Box H
Use of children's facilities in A&E

♦ **Restricted access to children's area**

One hospital studied had built a superb children's A&E department with its own separate waiting room, treatment and resuscitation areas, but it was only staffed for one afternoon shift per day. At other times, children had to wait in the adult waiting room or alongside adults in corridors.

♦ **Out of sight, out of mind**

The same children's area had no separately allocated medical staffing. Because it was so isolated from the adult treatment areas, some doctors waited until a 'sufficient number' of children were waiting before commencing treatment. Seriously ill children were frequently treated in the adult resuscitation room because some doctors were unfamiliar with the layout of equipment in the paediatric area.

♦ **Inadequate monitoring of children waiting for treatment**

At several hospitals studied it was difficult for nurses to supervise the condition of children in the separate waiting area. One newly opened children's facility was staffed only while a child was being treated. The children's waiting room is distant from the nurses' station and so can be used only by those whose condition is certain not to deteriorate.

♦ **Small and ill-equipped children's waiting rooms**

The children's waiting rooms at some hospitals studied are too small for parents to stay with their children and are not always within sight of the main waiting room. Some of those studied were ill equipped, particularly with toys or books suitable for school-age children. One contained only a broken rocking horse.

♦ **Children are not always shielded from distressing sights**

At one hospital studied, children had to pass through the 'major' treatment area on their way from the children's waiting room to the treatment cubicle.

♦ **Lack of separate short-stay observation areas for children**

Children who required a short period of observation before they are discharged were sometimes inappropriately admitted because there were no suitable facilities in A&E.

♦ **Split-site confusion**

At one trust studied, a children's hospital operated an unfunded 24-hour open-access walk-in emergency clinic and received medical emergencies. However, it had no out-of-hours X-ray facilities and did not have the equipment or expertise to set fractures or deal with any injuries other than the most trivial. More serious injuries were referred to the main A&E department. This was located half an hour away with no on-site paediatric support (other than in intensive care), children's nurses or children's beds. There was no clear guidance to tell parents where they should take injured children.

Psychologically disturbed patients

70. A&E departments frequently treat patients who are psychologically disturbed. These include people who have tried to commit suicide as well as those with a chronic psychiatric illness, often compounded by social problems, abuse of drugs or alcohol. Because they provide a 24-hour medical presence, A&E departments are still sometimes inappropriately regarded by the police as a 'place of safety' where patients can be held pending assessment by a psychiatrist and approved social worker under the Mental Health Act. The demands made by these patients on staff time and facilities can seriously affect the treatment of others.

71. It is widely agreed that mentally ill patients receive poor care in A&E departments. Few A&E doctors and nurses have training in how to treat them or when referral to a psychiatrist is appropriate. Psychiatric support to A&E was inadequate at all except the one hospital studied which had an on-site psychiatric unit.

72. Psychiatrists' responsibilities are often organised geographically. There can be difficulties first identifying and then contacting the team which covers a patient's usual place of residence. Several different psychiatrists may have to be summoned if more than one patient needs to be referred. There can then be a considerable delay before a psychiatrist arrives: one hospital reported four- to five-hour waits.

73. Development of a good psychiatric crisis intervention service for patients, which is not accessed through A&E, should be a priority. This would improve care for psychologically disturbed patients, reduce the risk of violent incidents in A&E, and make more appropriate use of facilities.

74. As a worthwhile interim measure, a psychiatric liaison nurse may be stationed in A&E to carry out a preliminary assessment of patients and make appropriate referrals, saving the time of A&E doctors and nurses and of the psychiatric teams (Case Study 7).

Case Study 7
A psychiatric liaison nurse in A&E

The Royal Sussex Hospital has a psychiatric liaison nurse jointly funded by A&E and the local community health trust. She is on call throughout the district and works closely with the social workers, but is based in the A&E department. She deals mainly with patients who try to commit suicide, but also with depressed, anxious or psychotic patients and alcoholics undergoing withdrawal who require a considerable nursing input. Many referrals come from attending rounds on the A&E observation ward. Her main task is to assess patients and to decide whether to refer them immediately to the duty psychiatrist, to a community psychiatric nurse, or organise an outpatient appointment.

The liaison nurse also teaches in the department, including advising A&E staff on how they should deal with violent patients.

By Accident or Design
Improving A&E Services in England and Wales

Case Study 8
Care of the bereaved

At the Norfolk and Norwich Hospital, there are two well-furnished relatives' rooms close to the resuscitation room with facilities for making drinks and telephone calls. A&E nurses also provide a bereavement follow-up service. Families are given a card with the name of the nurse and a bereavement booklet written specially for the department. The named nurse telephones them the next day. People can arrange to come back to see the nurse who looked after their relative and the consultant or registrar to discuss the circumstances and results of the post-mortem. The nurses were apprehensive about undertaking this role at first, but now find it rewarding. If the contact becomes too stressful, the nurse refers the families to the social worker attached to A&E who is trained in bereavement counselling and works with both relatives and staff.

Care of the bereaved

75. About 1 in 400 A&E patients either die while in A&E or are brought in dead. A survey conducted by the Royal College of Nursing and the BAEM in 1993 (Ref. 23) found that only 35 per cent of A&E units had a written departmental policy for the care of the bereaved. Only 10 per cent of these included management of telephone enquires. Few departments have a member of staff specifically assigned the task of caring for bereaved relatives. A number of the hospitals studied were taking action to improve this aspect of care. A few go further and take a major part in bereavement follow-up (Case Study 8).

Finding out what GPs and the public think

76. Patients are prepared to put up with a great deal provided that they receive effective clinical treatment, and warmly appreciate the efforts of hard-pressed staff. It is therefore not surprising that formal complaints about treatment in the A&E departments studied were comparatively rare and were greatly outnumbered by letters of appreciation. All A&E departments therefore need some other, proactive mechanism for ascertaining the opinions of patients, carers and their GPs.

77. The NHS Executive has recently published a booklet on patient perceptions of the quality of treatment in A&E (Ref. 24). Five of the eleven hospitals studied by the Audit Commission had commissioned local surveys to find out what patients thought of the service provided by their A&E departments (an example is given in Box I). However, only one had a programme of regular patient satisfaction studies covering both A&E and emergency admission procedures. Examples of issues raised by these opinion surveys include:

♦ difficulties of communicating with receptionists through glass screens, especially for patients in wheelchairs;

♦ dirty waiting areas and poorly maintained toilet facilities;

♦ regimented chairs and waits in uncomfortable places such as corridors;

♦ lack of privacy;

Box I
Patient satisfaction surveys

A survey commissioned by one A&E department took the form of semi-structured interviews with patients, relatives and friends to find out what kind of issues most concerned them, followed by a questionnaire to quantify their A&E experiences and views. Patients were interviewed as they were leaving the A&E department, except for those admitted to hospital who were followed up 24 hours later. The survey found that respondents most wanted improvements in the speed and efficiency of service, with more staff and doctors, but they also considered a better environment to be important.

Improvements most wanted by patients

A&E patients at this department most wanted improvements to the speed and efficiency of service, but also a better environment.

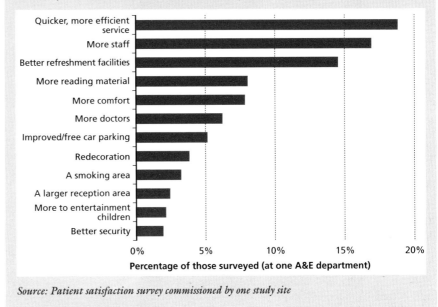

Source: Patient satisfaction survey commissioned by one study site

- the non-availability of refreshments;
- inadequate car-park security and safe access to public transport at night; and
- lack of information on reasons for delays in treatment.

Research is now needed into ways of determining patient views and experiences that have proved most useful in influencing clinical or administrative procedures and the development of departmental facilities.

78. This chapter has suggested a number of ways of improving the quality of care and patient experience in A&E. However, A&E departments do not and cannot exist in isolation. Chapter 3 shows that if they are to function efficiently and effectively, they must relate closely not only to the rest of the hospital but also to pre-hospital care.

Recommendations

Health commissioning bodies should:

1   promote inter-hospital audit and external review (Para. 56); and

2   facilitate the development of psychiatric crisis intervention not accessed through A&E (Para. 73).

Acute hospital trusts with A&E departments should:

Information

3   audit and improve the accuracy, timeliness and usefulness of information sent to GPs (Para. 62);

4   ensure that A&E patients receive good written instructions and information on discharge (Para. 63); and

5   establish mechanisms for understanding patients' views of A&E (Para. 76).

Procedures

6   ensure that there is a regular programme of inter-specialty and inter-disciplinary clinical and procedural audit (Para. 56);

7   screen and follow up frail patients discharged directly from A&E (Para. 64);

8   allocate responsibility for raising awareness of children's issues (Para. 67); and

9   establish a policy for care of the bereaved (Para. 75).

Staffing

10 ensure that SHOs have access to experienced support at night and weekends (Paras. 53, 55);

11 ensure that a paediatrician is available on-call 24 hours per day and look for ways to increase the number of sick children's nurses in A&E (Para. 67); and

12 ensure that A&E departments have adequate access to psychiatric support (Paras. 73, 74).

Facilities

13 ensure there are separate, properly equipped and staffed waiting and treatment areas for children, available 24 hours a day (Para. 69).

3 Working with Other Specialties

A&E departments do not always receive timely back up from other specialties and services to support diagnosis, plan admissions, and assist with the initial care of the critically ill or injured.

A&E cannot solve the problem of slow emergency admission without help. A patient may wait to be seen by a specialty doctor, for tests to be completed, for a vacant bed, for a porter or for transport. One senior manager must be responsible for initiatives to reduce delays, but the plan of action needs to be agreed with clinicians from *all* specialties, managers and referring GPs.

Resuscitation of severely injured patients needs to be carried out by a defined team with clear roles, trained in a standard methodology such as ATLS.

79. A&E departments need day and night access to support from a wide range of other specialties and services which help with diagnosis, offer specialist expertise, plan emergency inpatient admissions, assist with the initial care of the critically ill or injured, and screen referrals. A series of reports has specified those specialties and services which should ideally be co-located with A&E and those which should have close links with it (Exhibit 19, Appendix 8).

Exhibit 19
The A&E galaxy

A series of reports has specified specialties and support services which should be co-located with A&E and those which should have close links with it.

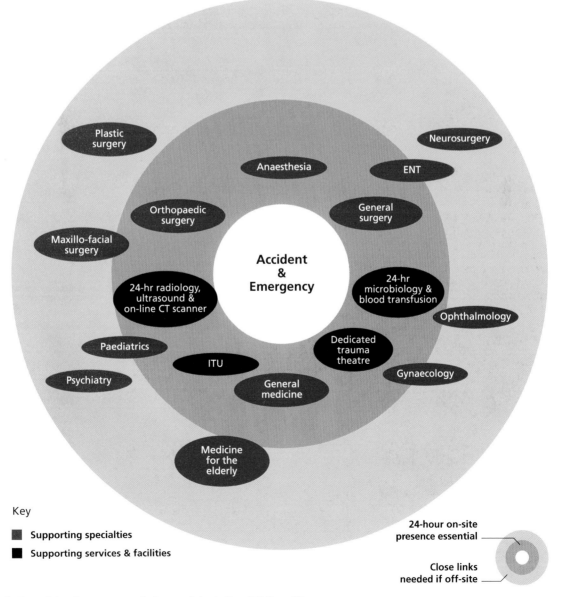

Source: Audit Commission from recommendations made by the Royal College of Surgeons, etc

80. This chapter reviews two aspects of an A&E department's functioning which are critically dependent on its links to the rest of the hospital:

◆ admission to an inpatient bed; and

◆ the initial care of the most severely ill or injured patients.

In both of these areas, structural, procedural and communications problems may need to be addressed.

Admission to an inpatient bed

"There is a major problem processing admissions in A&E because of limited space and time, and above all difficulty in finding beds. When patients wait for specialty attention, or for a bed, they do not distinguish the reason; they just lump it all together as the horribly long wait they had in A&E. Criticism is directed at A&E, not at the component parts."

Source: Interview with an A&E nurse at one of the hospitals studied

81. There was great variation between hospitals studied in the speed of admission to inpatient beds through A&E departments (Exhibit 20). Some hospitals had undertaken their own audits. One showed that patients whose arrival had been notified by a GP and pre-accepted by specialties waited just as long in A&E before admission as did self-presenting patients. Such findings echo those of the Clinical Standards Advisory Group whose recent study of emergency admissions (Ref. 3) also included patients admitted directly to wards.

82. A&E departments can do little on their own to solve the problem of waits for emergency admission. They need help from other specialties. Yet the magnitude of the problem is not often obvious to specialty consultants who seldom visit A&E. Lack of beds is not the only possible reason for delays. There may be sufficient beds overall, but just not available at the right times

Exhibit 20
Time to admission

There is great variation in the speed of admission to inpatient beds through A&E.

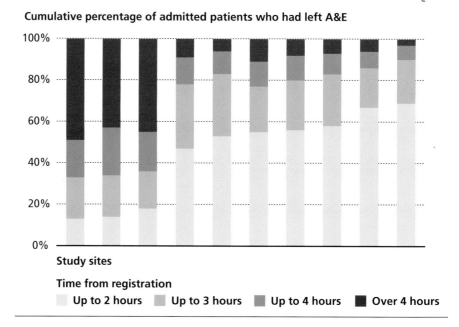

Cumulative percentage of admitted patients who had left A&E

Study sites

Time from registration

Up to 2 hours   Up to 3 hours   Up to 4 hours   Over 4 hours

Source: Audit Commission site visits

'A senior manager must be responsible for promoting and co-ordinating initiatives to reduce delays in emergency admissions through A&E and ensuring that benefits are delivered.'

of day. Patients may also have to wait in A&E to be seen by specialty doctors, for tests to be completed, for a porter or for transport. The consequent 'trolley waits' can result in logjams of patients filling every A&E cubicle, spilling over into corridors, theatres and resuscitation rooms, with inevitable knock-on effects on the speed, level of supervision and quality of care received by *all* A&E patients. If the numbers of emergency admissions through A&E continue to rise, this problem will become even more endemic.

83. Considering the prominence of the 'trolley waits' issue, there are surprising gaps in the information available on when specialty doctors are requested, when they arrive, when a decision is made to admit the patient, when a bed is requested, and when the patient leaves A&E for a ward. A new Patient's Charter standard was introduced in 1995 governing the time from decision to admit to arrival on the ward,[1] but this measure is not ideal, being open to manipulation. A decision to admit can be delayed until a bed is found. The patient may not be aware when this decision is made. Further, a succession of temporary beds on inappropriate wards, often with insufficient nursing and medical cover to care for acutely ill patients, may be less desirable than a longer wait in A&E. Total time from arrival in the hospital to placement in a staffed bed would therefore be a more robust indicator. But the Charter standard *will* bring this problem to the top of the management agenda and ensure that more complete and accurate data are collected, as will the surveys of 'trolley waits' now being conducted by community health councils and others in metropolitan areas.

Tackling trolley waits

84. There are no simple solutions to reducing waits for admission. Piecemeal action is unlikely to be sufficient; rather, a number of inter-related problems must be tackled (Exhibit 21, overleaf). A senior manager must be responsible for promoting and co-ordinating relevant initiatives and ensuring the benefits are delivered. Their first task should be to organise an inter-specialty audit to establish the scale of delays at different times of the day and week and the specialties involved. The most important contributory reasons can then be identified. These may differ by specialty. The main problem in one may be on-take rosters, in another the timing of discharge or of planned admissions. But, whatever the problems identified, it is crucial to establish joint ownership by clinicians from *all* specialties, as well as managers and referring GPs. A plan of action must be agreed jointly and its implementation reviewed regularly.

[1]
From April 1996, this time limit
will be 2 hours.

By Accident or Design
Improving A&E Services in England and Wales

Exhibit 21
Reducing trolley waits in A&E

A number of inter-related problems must be tackled and initiatives co-ordinated by a senior manager. But establishing joint ownership of the problem by all specialties is central.

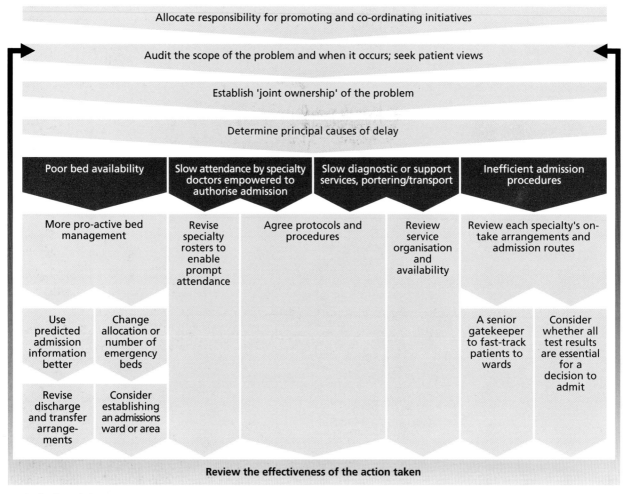

Source: Audit Commission

Possible components include:

◆ establishing protocols or introducing a hospital standing order requiring specialty doctors to attend A&E within set time limits (Case Study 9);

◆ improving the rostering of doctors from each inpatient specialty team responsible for emergency admissions and reviewing these doctors' other commitments during periods when they are 'on-take' (Case Study 10);

◆ locating in A&E a senior doctor from each key admitting specialty to act as a 'gatekeeper', fast-tracking appropriate patients to a ward (Case Study 11): this cuts out unnecessary investigations prior to admission and reduces inappropriate use of beds (Ref. 25) as well as bringing forward definitive planning of patient care; and

◆ instituting pro-active bed-management (Case Study 12).

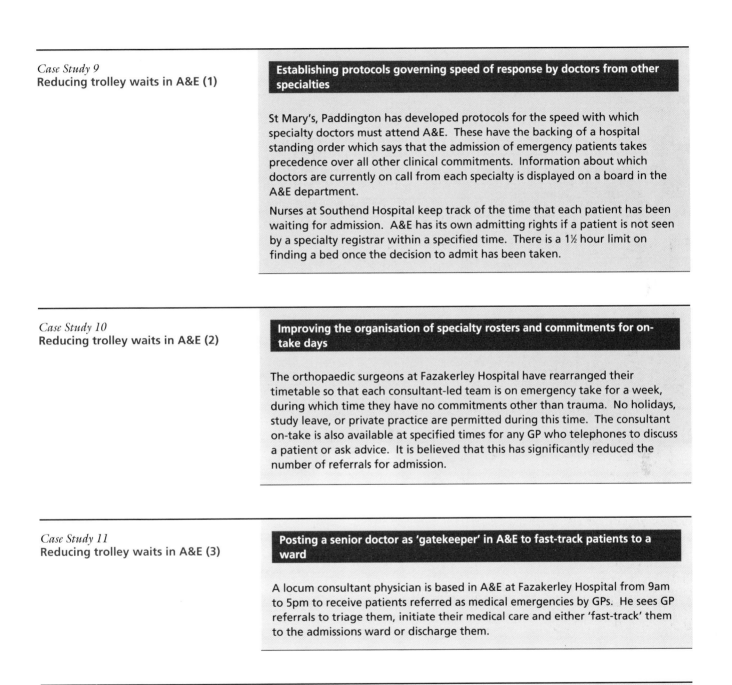

Case Study 9
Reducing trolley waits in A&E (1)

Establishing protocols governing speed of response by doctors from other specialties

St Mary's, Paddington has developed protocols for the speed with which specialty doctors must attend A&E. These have the backing of a hospital standing order which says that the admission of emergency patients takes precedence over all other clinical commitments. Information about which doctors are currently on call from each specialty is displayed on a board in the A&E department.

Nurses at Southend Hospital keep track of the time that each patient has been waiting for admission. A&E has its own admitting rights if a patient is not seen by a specialty registrar within a specified time. There is a 1½ hour limit on finding a bed once the decision to admit has been taken.

Case Study 10
Reducing trolley waits in A&E (2)

Improving the organisation of specialty rosters and commitments for on-take days

The orthopaedic surgeons at Fazakerley Hospital have rearranged their timetable so that each consultant-led team is on emergency take for a week, during which time they have no commitments other than trauma. No holidays, study leave, or private practice are permitted during this time. The consultant on-take is also available at specified times for any GP who telephones to discuss a patient or ask advice. It is believed that this has significantly reduced the number of referrals for admission.

Case Study 11
Reducing trolley waits in A&E (3)

Posting a senior doctor as 'gatekeeper' in A&E to fast-track patients to a ward

A locum consultant physician is based in A&E at Fazakerley Hospital from 9am to 5pm to receive patients referred as medical emergencies by GPs. He sees GP referrals to triage them, initiate their medical care and either 'fast-track' them to the admissions ward or discharge them.

Case Study 12
Reducing trolley waits in A&E (4)

Instituting pro-active bed-management

At St Mary's, bed management is seen as everyone's problem. All wards have an on-take rota for A&E admissions so that they can plan discharges and avoid moving patients around unnecessarily. SHOs liaise with the bed manager on the bed situation first thing each morning. If by the afternoon it is thought that there may be a bed shortage, a decision may be taken jointly by the most senior nurse, the most senior doctor in the hospital and the bed manager to bring forward the discharge of patients who would probably have gone home the following morning.

85. Some hospitals have found that establishing an admissions ward can reduce trolley waits provided that it has the full backing of specialties and its use is governed by sound protocols (Case Study 13, Exhibit 22). The advantages and disadvantages of such wards have not changed since they were listed in the Commission's Report on Management of Acute Beds, *Lying in Wait* (1992, Ref. 26, Appendix 9).

Case Study 13
A good admissions ward

The admissions ward at St Mary's, Paddington is located next to A&E and has 20 beds. Patients are normally admitted under specialty consultants. Patients with head injuries, for example, come in under the general surgeons for overnight observation. It is convenient to have all new patients on a ward close to A&E where they can be reviewed frequently by the registrars on take. However, the A&E consultants have authority to move people. An A&E consultant does a round each day before 10am to ensure that patients are moved on as soon as possible. A&E control of the admissions ward has been helpful in establishing its influence. The credibility of the A&E doctors stems from the way in which they relate to other services – particularly to consultant colleagues in other specialties – on subjects such as admissions. The admissions ward also provides an additional pool of nurses who may be available to help in A&E at times when it is exceptionally busy.

The admissions ward nurses plan short-term care over the first 48 hours and also start discharge planning. Normally the longest stays are 3 – 4 days (but terminally ill patients are not moved). Most patients arrive in the admissions ward between 5pm and 9am. During the day they are reassessed, transferred or discharged although, depending on the bed situation, additional patients may be admitted. The busiest time for the nurses is between 2 and 4pm (corresponding with a shift overlap) while patients are being transferred. Patients are accompanied by a nurse and introduced to the new ward.

Exhibit 22
Change in trolley waits on establishing an admissions ward

There are still some long waits at this hospital, but since the admissions ward opened, beds are now found more quickly for many patients.

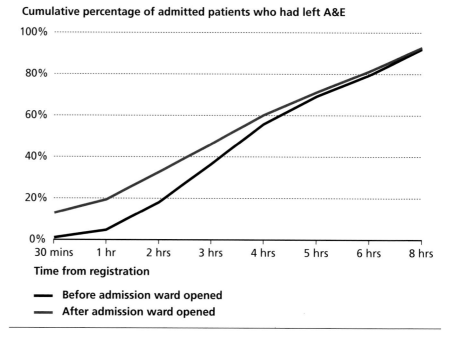

Cumulative percentage of admitted patients who had left A&E

Time from registration

— Before admission ward opened
— After admission ward opened

Source: Audit Commission – pilot audit

Initial care of the most severely ill or injured patients

86. Care of severely ill or injured patients must of course be fast, but it must also involve properly trained professionals with the right level of experience, and must be backed up by the right facilities. This applies not just to the hospital but to the process of getting the patient there in the first place.

87. In 1988 a Royal College of Surgeons' study (Ref. 27) showed that significantly more severely injured patients died in British hospitals than would have been expected on the basis of professional judgement or by international comparison. This stimulated major changes in the treatment of serious injury in Britain, many of which are still being implemented. Attention has focused in particular on:

◆ standardising the initial management of seriously injured patients;

◆ increasing the availability of relevant training;

◆ introducing comparative clinical audit; and

◆ developing pre-hospital care and the role of the paramedic.

Care once in hospital

88. There is a longstanding recommendation that hospitals should have a trauma team (Ref. 28). These teams have traditionally comprised doctors from A&E, anaesthetics, orthopaedics and general surgery, with nursing and radiographic support. This expertise should be available on-site 24 hours per day. The trauma team should come together at the outset of each resuscitation. Each member should have a defined role which may be broader than their own specialty. There should be a designated team leader and protocols governing circumstances in which more senior doctors from any specialty are called. All present should subscribe to standard principles such as Advanced Trauma Life Support (ATLS) and be competent in necessary procedures. Appropriate training is therefore essential for all doctors attending resuscitations, not just for A&E staff (Case Study 14, overleaf).

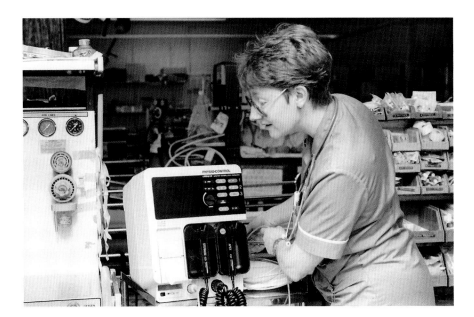

Case Study 14
**Treatment of major trauma by a
small A&E department**

The West Cumbria Hospital is small and in an isolated area with an above average incidence of major trauma. There are ITU and high dependency beds on site.

A clear strategy

When he was appointed, the A&E consultant initiated a multidisciplinary audit which also involved ambulance paramedics and local GPs involved in immediate care schemes. This set ground rules for trauma response, such as who would participate in the inter-specialty trauma team, maximum response times, use of ATLS methodology, and length of resuscitation.

Working as a team

The A&E consultant is personally involved as team leader in 80 per cent of responses to major trauma. Other team members include the first on-call consultant anaesthetist, middle-grade general and orthopaedic surgeons, an A&E SHO, two nurses and an assistant experienced in operation of the equipment. There are action cards for each team member. As well as contributing their own specialist skills, they also have broader roles. For instance, the orthopaedic surgeon is required to carry out general tasks in the initial stages of resuscitation and only uses specifically orthopaedic skills later. A doctor will contact his or her consultant if in doubt, or at the request of the team leader (since sometimes they feel embarrassed to do this). Nobody leaves a resuscitation until instructed to do so by the team leader. The trauma team specialties have a joint audit meeting at which they go through all trauma team cases.

Extending training to all

SHOs in A&E are given an introduction to ATLS methodology by the consultant. Middle-grade orthopaedic surgeons now receive similar training. The A&E consultant would like to extend this in-house training throughout all specialties which may be called to resuscitations.

Good relationships with regional specialties

Patients with severe head injuries are stabilised in A&E before a two-hour ambulance transfer. A&E has excellent relationships with the neurosurgeons who are usually in contact the next morning about any patient transferred for specialist neurological treatment. The neurosurgeons send A&E copies of documentation on discharge, supply all multiple trauma audit data and come to audit meetings. The links provide very beneficial feedback on the initial care of patients and their subsequent progress.

89. These conditions are not always met. For example:

♦ at two hospitals studied, it was left to the casualty doctor on duty, however inexperienced, to decide whether to call doctors from other specialties for cases of major trauma;

♦ at one of these hospitals (whose A&E department received patients brought in by emergency ambulance throughout the day and night), there were no CT scanning facilities, no on-site anaesthetic cover after midnight and at weekends, no ITU and no ventilated beds (other than in the resuscitation room).[1] Furthermore, there were no consultant or middle-grade A&E doctors in the department out of hours. This A&E department dealt very professionally and efficiently with the great majority of patients, but there must be severe doubts about its ability to treat satisfactorily the most severely injured, particularly at night;

[1]
This A&E department also lacked on-site support from consultant or middle grade physicians and all of the paediatricians were located at another hospital.

'Lack of accurate information about the condition of patients being brought in by ambulance can result in delay to treatment or to the trauma team being called unnecessarily.'

◆ four of the hospitals studied *had* established an inter-specialty trauma team, but many of the doctors attending from specialties other than A&E were not trained in the ATLS methodology. Some did not accept the concept of a team leader and saw no need to attend resuscitations until their own specialist contribution was required or to stay once it had been made.

90. The five A&E departments studied which had senior or middle-grade A&E doctors present during much of the day normally handled the initial stages of resuscitation themselves with an anaesthetist. They argued that doctors and nurses who are used to working together during the initial stages of resuscitation form a more effective team than one drawing on other specialties whose composition would vary from day to day. There may be merit in this, but it is nevertheless essential to ensure that an adequate response can be provided throughout the night and that doctors from other specialties are able to respond to calls from A&E quickly if requested.

Pre-hospital care

91. Treatment of major trauma and other emergency cases requires close integration of A&E services and pre-hospital care. A common complaint at the hospitals studied was a lack of accurate information about the condition of patients being brought in by ambulance. This could result in delay to treatment or to the trauma team being called unnecessarily. In a few cases, patients could have been taken directly to a unit with more appropriate facilities. Some ambulance control staff may not realise the importance of the observations that they are asked to relay or may be reluctant to tie up radio channels by activating 'talk-through' facilities between ambulances and A&E. One A&E department studied had no facilities for communication with ambulances. Documentation and handover to A&E staff by paramedics could also be improved in some areas.

92. In contrast, Norfolk ambulance crews routinely radio directly to the Norwich A&E unit details of the condition and expected arrival times of all patients, using an agreed format. The information is transcribed by receptionists and passed to the senior doctor on duty, who has the facility to question or advise crews directly. In Cumbria, the potential for relaying diagnostic test data for analysis before the patient reaches hospital is being explored. The London Ambulance Service is experimenting with ECG tests carried out by paramedics before patients with heart attacks are taken to hospital so that, if appropriate, they can be admitted more rapidly to a coronary care unit.

93. For A&E departments which lack essential supporting specialties or facilities, protocols should be agreed with ambulance services so that certain patients are taken to alternative hospitals which are able to offer appropriate services.

━━━━━━━━━━

94. A common theme running through this chapter and the previous one has been the availability of the right staff at the right time. It will not be possible to achieve this everywhere in the foreseeable future without more fundamental review of the way emergency care is provided to patients with differing types and severity of need. Chapter 4 therefore looks at the possibilities for more radical change.

Recommendations

The Department of Health and Welsh Office should:

1   revise the Patient's Charter standard so that the speed of admission to hospital through A&E is measured from a patient's arrival to placement in a staffed bed (Para. 83).

Health commissioning bodies should:

2   promote the closer integration of pre-hospital and A&E care for major trauma and other emergency cases (Paras. 91-93).

Acute hospital trusts with A&E departments should:

Information

3   audit the scale, timing and cause of any delays in each stage of the admission process and promote better recording of relevant information (Paras. 83, 84).

Procedures

4   allocate responsibility to a senior manager for implementing initiatives to reduce waits for admission, including agreeing an action plan with clinicians and managers from all receiving specialties and referring GPs (Para. 84);

5   agree protocols and revise emergency 'on-take' responsibilities to ensure a swift response to calls from A&E by doctors of appropriate seniority from inpatient specialties (Para. 84);

6   locate a senior doctor from key admitting specialties in A&E to ensure that appropriate patients are fast-tracked to a ward (Para. 84);

7   consider establishing an admissions ward if there are long delays in admission due to fluctuating bed availability (Para. 85);

8   ensure that essential support to A&E, including sufficient expertise and equipment for resuscitating and diagnosing severely injured patients, is readily available 24 hours a day (Paras. 88, 90);

9   ensure that trauma resuscitations are carried out by a defined team with clear roles according to a standard methodology such as ATLS (Paras. 88-90); and

10   improve communication facilities between A&E departments and ambulance crews to develop on-line diagnosis and enable a more prepared response by the receiving hospital (Paras. 91-93).

Pressures on emergency services are causing patients problems at many hospitals. Despite considerable scope for improvement within many existing A&E facilities, there remain significant quality problems which cannot be solved simply through additional funding, due to a shortage of doctors and nurses with the required skills.

Some change to the pattern of A&E services may be necessary to maintain even current standards, and more radical alternatives to A&E departments should be considered in the future to improve quality of care still further.

4 Looking to the Future

'Even if A&E departments and emergency arrangements at every hospital could be made to function as effectively and efficiently as at the best, major problems would remain which could be resolved only through more fundamental changes.'

95. So far, this report has considered the ways in which hospital emergency services are provided today. It has highlighted the fact that these services are under great pressure due to a sharp rise in the number of patients being referred for emergency hospital admission and shortages of skilled staff, both in A&E departments and in supporting specialties. This has led to significant problems for patients at many hospitals, such as:

- long waiting times for A&E treatment;

- delays in emergency admission, with some patients having to wait on trolleys in A&E departments for many hours;

- the inappropriate transfer of patients, some seriously ill, from one hospital to another simply to find a suitable vacant bed; and

- inadequate supervision of junior doctors at certain times of day, and the frequent unavailability of the right expertise at the right time.

Meanwhile, A&E departments are being urged to improve quality of care; for instance, by providing special facilities and dedicated trained staff for potentially vulnerable patients such as children. There are also pressures for a greater proportion of medical care to be provided by senior doctors rather than trainees.

96. As this report has demonstrated, there is significant scope to improve the services provided by many existing A&E facilities without the need for increased funding. In particular:

- rostering can often be improved so that there is a better match between staff availability and patient demand;

- the scope of nursing practice can be expanded and procedures modified to treat and discharge some patients more quickly;

- there is often room for better co-ordination with other hospital specialties and support services; and

- discharge information can be improved.

97. But even if A&E departments and emergency arrangements at every hospital could be made to function as effectively and efficiently as at the best, major problems would remain which could be resolved only through more fundamental changes, including:

- more trained A&E doctors and specialist A&E staff; for example, nurses trained to care for children;

- better access to specialist beds, including ITU; and

- provision of 24-hour on-site support from essential specialties and support services.

98. These problems cannot be solved in the short term simply through additional funding. For example, the availability of doctors and nurses with the required skills is limited. Consequently, some change to the current pattern of A&E services may be necessary to maintain even the present quality of care. This is likely to mean closing some smaller departments or developing them into minor injuries units, and concentrating full A&E services on fewer, larger sites. There is in any case some doubt as to whether the present configuration of emergency services is the best one. There are clearly difficult balances to be struck between maintaining (or improving) access to A&E services, providing better facilities and higher quality care, and treating patients efficiently. The debate should be drawn wider than the appropriate number and distribution of A&E departments, by considering whether some of their current functions could be better carried out elsewhere.

99. This chapter addresses these broader issues. It first examines the current size and location of major A&E departments and the scope for consolidation. It then discusses possible alternative provision and raises the issue of whether, in the longer term, A&E departments should continue to cater for such a wide range of disparate needs. Finally, it considers what needs to be done to initiate these changes, both at a national level and by authorities purchasing emergency care locally.

The number and location of A&E departments

100. A&E departments vary greatly in size: a few in remote areas see fewer than 10,000 new patients each year, while the largest sees almost 140,000. There is similar variation in the size of the hospitals in which they are located. Their geographical distribution reflects history as much as current need (Exhibit 23, overleaf).

101. An A&E department needs a certain minimum level of attendance to maintain the expertise of its doctors and nurses and to provide junior doctors with an adequate breadth of training and experience. It has been suggested that 35,000 patients a year is an appropriate minimum (Ref. 29). Yet one-quarter of major A&E units currently treat less than this number of people. It has also been claimed that a minimum of 50,000 is desirable if all the recommended supporting specialties, 24-hour support services and A&E facilities are to be provided cost-effectively (Ref. 30). But only one in three A&E departments are of this size (Exhibit 24, overleaf). Thus, many A&E departments have difficulty in providing a sustainable, high quality service because of their size, or because they lack essential specialist support on-site. Seriously ill patients are less likely to achieve a good outcome – including survival – if treated at small units where specialist expertise is less available.

By Accident or Design
Improving A&E Services in England and Wales

Exhibit 23
Geographical distribution of A&E departments

This reflects history as much as current need.

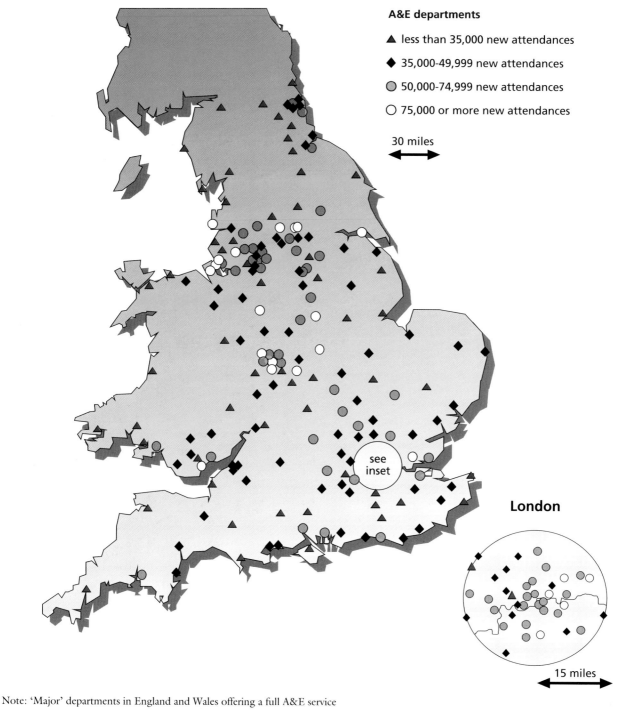

A&E departments

▲ less than 35,000 new attendances

◆ 35,000-49,999 new attendances

⬤ 50,000-74,999 new attendances

◯ 75,000 or more new attendances

30 miles

see inset

London

15 miles

Note: 'Major' departments in England and Wales offering a full A&E service

Source: Audit Commission, from surveys and directories

Exhibit 24
Size of A&E departments

One-quarter of A&E departments treat less than 35,000 new patients per year; only about 1 in 3 have 50,000 or more new attendances.

New attendances per year (000s) 1994/95

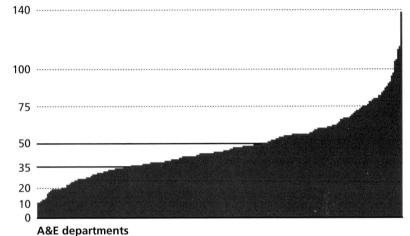

A&E departments

Sources: BAEM, Audit Commission surveys and trust financial returns

Note:
'Major' departments in England and Wales offering a full A&E service

102. Concentrating A&E services in fewer, larger departments offers the potential for short-term operational advantages and improved standards of care:

♦ it would be possible to increase the number of hours per week during which there are senior A&E doctors or specialist A&E staff (for example, nurses trained to care for children) on-site;

♦ the quality of training received by junior doctors could be improved, with consequent benefits for patients;

♦ it would be somewhat more straightforward to roster staff to match expected workload and to retain the flexibility to deal with unexpected demands; and

♦ more A&E departments would be sited in hospitals where supporting specialties and services are available.

103. The arguments for concentrating emergency services into fewer, larger A&E departments are thus based on quality of outcome rather than cost. The balance to be struck is between access for all patients (made easier by having many, smaller departments) and quality of treatment for the seriously injured (improved by larger centres).

104. Over half of all A&E departments are within ten miles of another hospital offering a full A&E service, and one-third, mostly in metropolitan areas, within five miles (Exhibit 25, overleaf). Admittedly, distance alone is only a starting point for assessing access to services. Local public transport facilities, traffic congestion and levels of access to cars must also be taken into account before rationalisation decisions are made. However, given the current size and location of A&E units, it is clear that the quality of emergency services could be improved by closing some smaller departments where there is good patient access to other facilities nearby.

Exhibit 25
Distribution of A&E departments

Over half of all A&E departments are within 10 miles of another hospital offering a full A&E service.

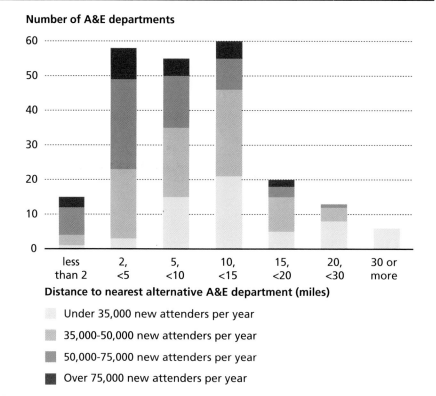

Number of A&E departments

Distance to nearest alternative A&E department (miles)

Under 35,000 new attenders per year

35,000-50,000 new attenders per year

50,000-75,000 new attenders per year

Over 75,000 new attenders per year

Source: Audit Commission, from surveys and directories

105. As explained earlier, the case for consolidating emergency services is not based on cost. Nonetheless, it has been suggested that rationalising provision would release resources and that these could be used for developing local facilities for treating minor injuries. But although A&E departments with high numbers of attendances do have slightly lower average costs per attendance than smaller ones,[I] these differences may reflect the lower proportionate overheads of clinical and administrative support to the A&E specialty in larger hospitals rather than economies due to the size of the A&E departments themselves. In other words, there is no conclusive evidence that amalgamating medium-sized departments would really release resources.

106. It is difficult and politically sensitive to close an A&E department. The concerns of patients and local clinicians must be addressed. Before a decision is made to close an A&E department there would need to be:

◆ an alternative location with better access to the necessary supporting specialties and services available 24 hours per day;

◆ well thought-out plans to enable the remaining A&E departments to cope with the increase in demand, including adequate access to theatres and intensive care, and provision of inpatient beds;

◆ consideration of the impact on the hospital where the A&E department is to close;

I
The reported cost per patient decreases by £1 (or about 2 per cent) per 10,000 additional annual A&E attendances, but there is considerable variation.

66

'Despite reservations, the quality arguments for rationalising emergency provision are sufficiently strong to recommend that reviews are initiated for all small A&E departments with good access to alternative facilities. Each situation will need to be assessed on its own merits.'

◆ provision for enhanced primary care or other services in the locality if required;

◆ effective two-way communication with the public to explain the rationale behind the changes and the impact on patients;

◆ focused patient and parent education to reduce demand for local emergency care; and

◆ mechanisms in place to evaluate the effect of the changes.

107. Small A&E departments in remote areas of the country pose a special problem. There are 14 units with fewer than 35,000 attendances per year located more than 20 miles from the nearest alternative. Although some of these small departments do not meet the full specification of larger A&Es,[1] many nevertheless provide a good service for the majority of patients attending and some are specifically equipped to deal with major disasters due to their location (eg, radiation contamination). But many argue that more seriously injured patients should be transported directly to larger A&E units with a full range of supporting services.

108. Reconfiguration of emergency services would also present challenges for hospitals which retained and expanded their A&E departments. In particular, these hospitals would need to be able to accommodate more emergency admissions. In consequence there would either be greater fluctuations in bed occupancy, which might mean that more beds were required, or an increase in the numbers of patients who had to be transferred to other hospitals after admission. Specialties would need to review their emergency on-take arrangements and responsibilities in the light of any changes in workload.

109. Despite these reservations, the quality arguments for rationalising emergency provision are sufficiently strong to recommend that reviews are initiated for all small A&E departments (with, say, less than 50,000 new attendances per year) where there is good access to alternative facilities (say, within ten miles). Each situation will need to be assessed on its own merits and specific local circumstances taken into account. The reviews should include the type of patients seen during the year, levels of staffing and facilities, and information on travel times within the catchment area and to other departments. If these reviews were to result in the amalgamation of 50 per cent of such small departments, this would mean closing 31 A&E units in England and Wales.

[1]
However small they are, A&E departments must be led by an A&E consultant and have adequate diagnostic facilities (specified in Chapter 3), arrangements for obtaining advice from all supporting specialties, and agreements for the transfer of those patients who require more specialist care.

By Accident or Design
Improving A&E Services in England and Wales

Alternative settings for emergency care

110. A&E departments are only one of a number of settings in which patients seeking urgent or emergency care could be treated (Exhibit 26):

◆ Further development of pre-hospital care for sick and injured patients could change thinking about the ideal location of emergency services.

◆ The most severely injured patients, making up no more than ½ per cent of attendances, could be treated in specialist centres.

◆ Some patients could be cared for in minor injuries units or specialist walk-in outpatient clinics, possibly within polyclinics.

◆ Expansion of primary care delivered by GPs and practice nurses in various settings could reduce the number of attendances at some A&E departments.

◆ Self-care can be extended through focused patient and parent education.

◆ Direct self-referral rather than A&E attendance may be appropriate for some conditions – eg, asthma.

◆ Emergency GP referrals could be handled by separate admissions areas or local admissions units.

Exhibit 26
The spectrum of emergency care

A&E departments are only one of the settings in which patients seeking urgent or emergency care could be treated.

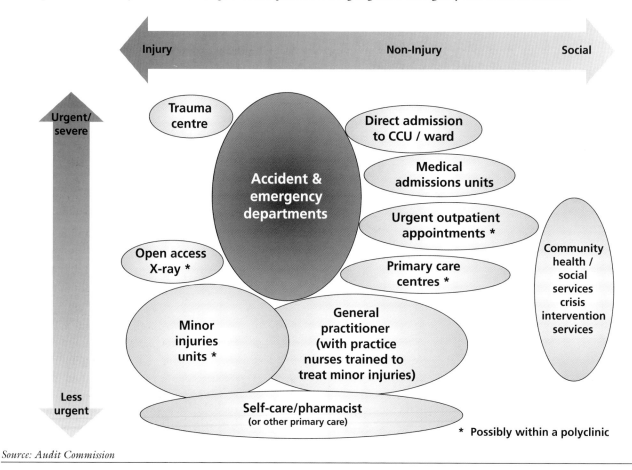

* Possibly within a polyclinic

Source: Audit Commission

'Further development of pre-hospital care for sick and injured patients could change thinking about the ideal location of emergency services.'

Each of these alternatives needs to be considered in the light of local and regional needs and circumstances. Individually, none is likely to be as flexible as an A&E department in its ability to deal with a wide spectrum of medical emergencies and injuries of differing severity at all hours of the day and night but, in combination, they offer the prospect both of better patient care and of a solution to many of the current staffing difficulties.

Pre-hospital care

111. The future of A&E departments will be affected by developments in the way that seriously ill patients are treated before they reach hospital. Speedy arrival of a trained paramedic, or better still of a doctor with appropriate skills, may often be more important than the length of time subsequently taken to get the patient to hospital. It is government policy that by 1996 the crews of all emergency ambulances should include at least one paramedic. Pre-hospital care has proved effective in reviving patients following heart attacks, but there is still debate as to whether treating injured patients at the roadside or in their homes is clinically beneficial and, if so, in what circumstances. Improved communications between ambulance crews and hospitals will increasingly influence the range of interventions that can be made before a patient reaches hospital. Wider use of remote electro-cardiographic testing of cardiac patients, for instance, may enable a decision to admit to be confirmed en route so that patients can be taken straight to a cardiac unit. Such developments would reduce the clinical advantages of having an A&E department close at hand for patients who are transported by ambulance, but would not serve the needs of those who currently choose not to wait for an ambulance.

Treating serious injuries

112. The debate continues over the clinical advantages and cost effectiveness of consolidating treatment for the small percentage of patients with serious multiple injuries into regional trauma centres. These would provide 24-hour consultant-based initial care and bring together on a single site all the specialties, including neurosurgery, needed for the definitive treatment of multiply injured patients. Such centres would act as the hub of a system of pre-hospital care and outlying A&E departments. An evaluation of the pilot trauma centre in North Staffordshire will be published early in 1996.

113. Trauma centres are not the only way to improve the care of seriously injured patients. An A&E or orthopaedic trauma consultant is on duty at the Oxford Radcliffe Hospital, day and night, to treat severely injured patients. Initial indications are that this has reduced subsequent lengths of hospital stay. Although this may not be appropriate in all locations, larger hospitals should consider having an orthopaedic consultant present in A&E (or an adjoining area) for a substantial proportion of the day. This would increase the level of advice available to A&E SHOs and speed orthopaedic admissions. It could also substantially reduce the number of patients who need to come back to a fracture clinic the next day. Although extra consultant resources would be required, junior doctor and nurse time would be saved and patients would receive a better and more convenient service.

Treating minor injuries

114. Minor injuries units, often run by nurse practitioners, have had apparent success in providing swift, high quality, local treatment for patients who do not need the full expertise and facilities of an acute hospital (Refs. 31-36). Use of telemedical facilities, such as a video link to hospital specialists, can make this service even more flexible and effective. Appendix 10 compares the advantages and disadvantages of three forms of minor injuries service. However, minor injuries units are not necessarily a cheap option. Although some evaluations show their average cost per attendance to be less than half those of A&E departments (Ref. 37), others suggest little difference. But care must be taken in interpreting cost comparisons. Most minor injuries patients need fewer investigations and less staff resource than the average attender at a major department, which also has to treat seriously ill patients. A study at the Edinburgh Royal Infirmary suggests that, on average, it cost 60 per cent less to treat patients in the examination room (their minor injuries area) than other A&E attenders. Major departments also have to bear their share of the higher overheads of an acute hospital site. Also, between 10 and 20 per cent of minor injuries patients are referred for further treatment in major A&Es, at additional cost. For all these reasons, any reductions in A&E attendance numbers through provision of alternative facilities for treating minor injuries would not be reflected pro rata in the expenditure of A&E departments.

Developments in primary care

115. Some large general practices are investing in X-ray equipment and other diagnostic facilities which may reduce the need for A&E attendance. This trend is likely to be accelerated if current projects to give large fundholding practices budgets for emergency care are judged to be successful. Practices in these schemes will have a financial incentive both to provide their own alternative outpatient and telephone advice services, and to reduce 'inappropriate' A&E attendance by their patients. The impact of this development may be limited by GPs' current relative lack of experience in treating injuries, by the cost of providing practice facilities to undertake a wider range of treatments, and by the ability of practices to absorb additional consultations.

116. A growing number of GP co-operatives provide primary care out of surgery hours. Most operate a rota of doctors undertaking home visits, backed up by sophisticated communications facilities and transport. Many also staff a well-equipped night centre where patients who are able to travel can be examined in a secure environment. Although these services are primarily designed to reduce the number of home visits made by GPs at night, fewer patients are advised to attend A&E and the centres are used for simple emergency treatments not requiring hospital facilities. A pilot scheme in Medway was estimated to have reduced the number of A&E attendances substantially (Ref. 38). A number of hospital trusts are now considering providing such centres adjacent to A&E departments (Ref. 39). This would have the advantage that a rota of local GPs could work independently, but in close co-operation with A&E consultants and with ready access to hospital diagnostic facilities, but it misses an important opportunity to relocate services closer to the patients.

117. Some hospitals in areas with a transient population and less developed general practices employ GPs within their A&E departments specifically to see patients identified as needing primary care.[1] Proponents claim that GPs provide better care because their experience enables them to take a more rounded view of patients' needs (Refs. 10, 40). They also order fewer tests than SHOs, but they are paid at close to consultant rates and so cost more to employ than other A&E doctors. Neither have they proved effective in persuading patients to use their own GPs rather than an A&E department in future. These services will need to be reviewed now that they can no longer be funded from primary care budgets.

118. Schemes to improve access to social care in night-time crises and over weekends are also proving valuable to patients, as well as reducing A&E attendance and emergency hospital admission. The voluntary sector has an expanding role in providing this crisis care.

Facilitating informed self-care and first-aid

119. Although the vast majority of A&E patients have sound reasons for attending, there is anecdotal evidence that people are becoming less willing to treat minor injuries and symptoms themselves. On the one hand this is ascribed to lack of confidence, particularly among young mothers in deprived areas, compounded by the breakdown of extended families who can provide advice and reassurance. On the other hand, it is said to result from increased expectations of the health service, together with growing awareness of possible complications and legal liability on the part of carers, schools and businesses if medical advice is not sought.

120. If more self-care is to be encouraged, it must be appropriate and informed. It is essential to educate both children and adults in a focused way. Access to telephone advice on first aid and whether to seek further care is also needed in the event of an emergency. Outcomes of more serious injuries and medical emergencies could also be improved if the public were better informed about action required while waiting for professional help. Self-care would also be fostered by expanding out-of-hours community pharmacy services where patients could seek advice and obtain certain medicines and dressings.

Self-referral direct to inpatient specialties

121. It may be more appropriate for certain patients who have an established relationship with a particular specialty or department to approach them directly in emergencies. This already happens in some places and:

♦ reduces congestion in A&E;

♦ eliminates the need for the patient to wait in the A&E department;

[1]
As distinct from employing GPs as clinical assistants who may treat any A&E patient.

71

'Fundamental data on which to base decisions about the future of emergency care are still lacking.'

- saves time for the specialist doctor who would otherwise be called to A&E;

- ensures that the patient is seen in the first instance by a relevant specialist;

- increases the likelihood that the patient will be seen by someone who knows them and their medical history.

Conditions for which this system may be appropriate include asthma, early pregnancy and genito-urinary medicine.

Emergency GP admissions

122. In order to improve the care of patients referred by GPs for emergency admission, it might be advantageous to establish an admissions area separate from the main A&E department where they could be examined before transfer to a ward. In some localities, it might also prove desirable to develop admission units at hospitals other than the A&E site. However, it would be important to ensure that such admission units were adequately staffed and equipped to care for patients whose condition might deteriorate, and also that they did not, as has sometimes occurred, come to be regarded by the local population as 'unofficial A&E departments'.

The way forward

Evidence-based decisions

123. The previous sections have discussed the need to rationalise emergency services and described a range of approaches which could potentially complement or replace traditional A&E departments. There has recently been a welcome expansion of research into aspects of emergency care; for instance, on the effectiveness of paramedic care for injured patients. The NHS Anglia and Oxford region emergency care project has also published the results of a consultation exercise of clinicians in that region which was informed by a comprehensive review of the research findings currently available (Refs. 41 and 42). However, fundamental data on which to base decisions about the future of emergency services are still lacking. To date, there has been little evaluation following A&E closures or amalgamations, so the effects on the local population, on waiting times for treatment, or on total NHS costs remain unclear.

124. Further research is also needed on the facilities and skills required to meet the full range of emergency needs. There are, as yet, no clear answers to such questions as: 'What factors are most important in determining a good clinical outcome?' and 'How many patients does a department, or an individual doctor, need to see in order to gain or maintain clinical competence in treating a specific condition?' More work is needed to determine safe medical response times and travel times, and to establish what proportion of emergency patients needs to be treated at a hospital rather than at a minor injuries unit or GP surgery. Such knowledge is essential for planning the distribution of A&E departments and alternative facilities.

Integrated planning

'Planning needs to be co-ordinated at regional level.'

125. The advent of purchasing agencies provides an opportunity for integrated planning of primary and hospital emergency care according to the needs of the local population. Decisions about the location of A&E departments are integral to those about the distribution and scope of other local services. They cannot be made in isolation, or even just as part of the primary care continuum. But even with the integration of primary and secondary commissioning, the geographical fragmentation of responsibility for purchasing emergency care compounds the difficulty of formulating strategies and bringing about major change.

126. Planning needs to be co-ordinated at regional level to achieve an optimal distribution of emergency care facilities for a population wider than that of a single commissioning agency's patch. In particular, it would be advantageous for at least one hospital in each area to have access (preferably on-site) to sub-regional specialties such as neurosurgery, plastic surgery and cardio-thoracic surgery. This 'major' site would need to serve a large local population but also offer good access to a wider catchment area for which referral criteria and funding arrangements would have to be developed. There may also be scope for large A&E departments in neighbouring trusts within metropolitan areas to specialise in particular conditions, as well as providing a general A&E service, as has been proposed in Leeds (Ref. 43). Appropriate use should be made of input from geographers, urban planners and epidemiologists to inform the planning process.

Convincing the public and clinicians

127. Proposals to reconfigure hospital services which involve closing an A&E department rightly arouse considerable public and political debate. There are major issues to be addressed:

◆ Alternative local facilities for treating minor injuries and out-of-hours medical emergencies must be widely publicised and win public acceptance before plans to close a unit are finalised. In many areas, these local services will need to include facilities for X-ray and the follow-up of simple fractures.

◆ Emergency admission arrangements must be reviewed fully before A&E services are withdrawn.

◆ There must be widespread support from clinical staff.

◆ Ambulance services must be capable of providing an adequate service to persuade the public that patients with serious illnesses or injuries will not be put at risk by the closure.

Conclusion

128. The current pressures on accident and emergency services are a microcosm of those faced by the NHS as a whole. But the deficiencies described in this report require priority attention if public confidence is to be retained in the ability of the NHS to meet what are seen as basic needs when accidents and emergencies, whether minor or major, occur. Implementing the measures proposed in Chapters 1 and 2 of this report would bring some relief from current pressures, but there is a limit to what A&E departments can do to improve emergency care without the active co-operation of other hospital specialties and support services. Purchasers and those providing primary and pre-hospital care also have a part to play, by listening to patients' concerns and setting up alternatives to A&E which better meet the needs of those who do not specifically require the skills and facilities of a major hospital. Only in this way can A&E departments be freed up to do the job which they are best equipped to perform, without compromising the care of other patients.

Recommendations

The Department of Health and the Welsh Office should:

1 establish and support mechanisms for assisting strategic change at regional level;

2 take steps to meet the resource requirements of supporting an effective emergency service, in particular specialist staff and inpatient beds;

3 set the research agenda to build a robust knowledge base for decisions about the future of emergency care:
- optimum approaches for meeting the full range of emergency needs,
- how patient views can be ascertained in a way which is useful to improve care,
- cost and quality of alternative forms of emergency service;

4 improve education to facilitate informed self-care and first aid, as well as more appropriate use of alternative facilities for emergency care; and

5 communicate to the public the need for change in the organisation and use of A&E departments.

Health commissioning bodies should:

6 establish the needs of the local population for all types of emergency care, in consultation with A&E and primary care clinicians, and the public;

7 audit the activity of small A&E departments with respect to the type of cases seen, staff and facilities with a view to merging the least safe and viable;

8 review the current configuration in conjunction with neighbouring purchasers and explore opportunities to rationalise emergency care;

9 develop and publicise alternative modes of emergency care (including the provision of primary care outside normal surgery hours) before A&Es are closed;

10   review emergency admission arrangements to ensure the availability of sufficient beds on, or close to, the A&E site; and

11   evaluate the effects of changes to emergency provision on access, quality of care and efficiency.

Glossary

ATLS	Advanced trauma life support (procedure/courses).
BAEM	British Association for Accident and Emergency Medicine.
CAS Card	Casualty card – colloquial name for A&E patient notes.
CCU	Coronary Care Unit.
CSAG	Clinical Standards Advisory Group – published a major study of emergency hospital admissions in 1995.
CT	Computerised tomography – X-raying in different planes.
ECG	Electro-cardiogram readings.
ITU	Intensive Therapy Unit.
MIU	Minor Injuries Unit.
NAI	Non accidental injury (to a child, etc).
(Emergency) Nurse Practitioner ENP	An experienced nurse, trained and authorised to diagnose, treat and discharge or refer certain patients within agreed protocols on his/her own responsibility without reference to a doctor.
OT	Occupational therapist.
Paramedic	Ambulance person with extended qualifications in providing pre-hospital care according to protocols.
PAS	Patient administration system.
RSCN	Registered Sick Children's Nurse.
SHO	Senior house officer – the lowest post-registration medical training grade.
Suturing	Stitching up a wound.
Trauma	Injury.

Triage	Categorisation of a patient's need for emergency treatment according to its urgency or nature. In A&E departments, commonly carried out by a nurse either as part of the initial assessment or after registration. Categories differ, but are usually similar to the following:

1: Immediate – life threatening.

2: Urgent – possibility of rapid deterioration.

3: Less time-critical injury or condition appropriate to A&E.

4: Long-standing condition more appropriate to primary care.

Appendix 1: Acknowledgements

External advisory group

Dr Howard Baderman	A&E Adviser to the Department of Health A&E Consultant, University College Hospital, London
Mr Gautam Bodiwala	A&E Consultant, Leicester Royal Infirmary
Ms Kate Burgess	Clinical Director & Nurse Manager A&E, Southend Hospital
Mr Steven Clarke	Director of Finance, Cambridgeshire Health Commission
Mr Christopher Cutting	President BAEM, A&E Consultant, Taunton & Somerset Hospital
Mr Brian Dolan	Clinical Researcher, A&E Primary Care Service, Kings College School of Medicine & Dentistry
Mr David Gilbert/ Dr Michael McGovern	Acute Services Policy Unit, Department of Health
Mrs Linda Lamont	Patients' Association
Mr Jonathan Marrow	Chairman, BAEM Clinical Services Committee, A&E Consultant, Arrowe Park Hospital.
Mr Peter McGinity	Secretary, A&E Reference Group, London Implementation Group Projects Director, St Mary's Hospital.
Prof. Jon Nicholl	Deputy Director, University of Sheffield Medical Care Research Unit
Prof. Tony Redmond	A&E Consultant, North Staffordshire Trauma Centre
Ms Jo Rodin	Chair, Bexley & Greenwich Health Commissioning Agency
Dr David Salter	Welsh Office
Mrs Rosemary Wilkinson	Royal College of Nursing Accident & Emergency Association
Mr Keith Willett	Trauma Consultant, John Radcliffe Hospital, Oxford
Mr Andrew Wooding	Director of Finance, Nottingham University Hospital

---

Miss Fionna Moore	Clinical Adviser to Audit Commission A&E Study Team A&E Consultant, John Radcliffe Hospital, Oxford

Main study site visits were conducted at:
Aintree Hospitals NHS Trust (Fazakerley)
Bolton Hospitals NHS Trust (Bolton Royal Infirmary)
Brighton Healthcare NHS Trust (Royal Sussex County Hospital)
Ceredigion & Mid-Wales NHS Trust (Bronglais Hospital, Aberystwyth)
Edinburgh Royal Infirmary NHS Trust
Royal Hull Hospitals NHS Trust (Hull Royal Infirmary)
Llanelli & Dinefwr NHS Trust (Prince Philip Hospital)
Norfolk & Norwich Health Care NHS Trust
St Mary's Hospital NHS Trust, London
Southend Healthcare NHS Trust
West Cumbria Healthcare NHS Trust (Whitehaven)

**Shorter study visits were made to
A&E departments at the following hospitals:**
Arrowe Park Hospital
Hope Hospital
Kingston upon Thames Hospital
Leicester Royal Infirmary
Lewisham Hospital
North Staffordshire Royal Infirmary
Oxford Radcliffe Hospital
Royal Free Hospital
Royal Liverpool University Hospital
Royal London Hospital
Cardigan Minor Injuries Unit
St Charles Minor Injuries Unit
Workington Minor Injuries Unit

Pilot audits were carried out at:
Bedford Hospitals NHS Trust
Countess of Chester Hospital NHS Trust
The Homerton Hospital NHS Trust
The King's Mill Centre for Health Care Services NHS Trust
Milton Keynes Hospital NHS Trust
Morriston Hospital NHS Trust
Southmead Health Services NHS Trust
Winchester and Eastleigh Healthcare NHS Trust

We would also like to thank the following individuals and organisations for their assistance:
Prof. Ken Boffard (Johannesburg General Hospital)
Ms Sue Burr (Royal College of Nursing)
Ms Jillian Daly & Mr Andrew Corbett-Nolan (South Thames RHA)
Prof. Miles Irving (University of Manchester, Hope Hospital)
Prof. Brian McKibbin (University of Wales)
Prof. Stephen Miles (Royal London Hospital)
Ms Aileen Murphy & Ms Bronagh Walton (National Audit Office)
Mr Frank Plani (Johannesburg General Hospital)
Prof. Colin Roberts (University of Wales)
Ms Sue Williams (Merton, Sutton & Wandsworth FHSA)
Ms Marilyn Woodford (Director, Major Trauma Outcome Study)
Dr Kevin Woods (formerly Regional Director, Trent RHA)
Prof. David Yates (University of Manchester, Hope Hospital)
Lincolnshire Ambulance Trust

Other individuals and organisations who commented on the draft report included:
Association of Community Health Councils for England and Wales
British Medical Association
General Medical Council
Healthcare Financial Management Association
National Association of Health Authorities and Trusts
National Audit Office
NHS Executive
NHS Trust Federation
Nuffield Institute for Health
Patients Association
Royal College of Nursing
University of Edinburgh Department of Medicine
Welsh Office

Appendix 2: Comparing Unit Costs of A&E Treatment

The relative efficiency of A&E departments is often judged by comparing trusts' A&E specialty costs per attendance. Yet the NAO found in 1992 that there was no reliable, collated information on the cost of A&E services nationally. The current study confirms the difficulty of drawing valid comparisons about differences in unit costs derived either from trust financial returns or from A&E departmental budgets:

◆ Reported A&E attendance figures may be misleading.

◆ Case-mix differs, as do boundaries between A&E and inpatient care.

◆ Returns for many trusts include peripheral A&E or minor injuries units.

◆ The costs of support services such as radiology, pathology and pharmacy are often allocated between departments on a historical basis.

◆ Allocation of trust overheads over which A&E has no control, including site capital charges, may distort comparisons.

New attendances: Some patients treated by staff who are not on the A&E budget, sometimes even by staff who are not funded by the trust, may be counted as A&E attendances. Examples include patients seen by primary care doctors in A&E departments and those referred at initial assessment in A&E directly to walk-in paediatric or other specialty clinics.

Return and clinic attendances: These are counted inconsistently. Classification of clinics as A&E or outpatient varies. Second and subsequent reviews may be omitted. Unbooked returns may be counted as an additional attendance or as a continuation of the first attendance. Some A&E consultants still run unfunded minor operating sessions.

Differences in case-mix: Unit costs take no account of case-mix, which varies widely from one hospital to another. Certain categories of expenditure can be particularly affected. One study site sees an unusually high proportion of patients with acute cardiac conditions requiring the swift administration of expensive drugs.

Departmental layout: Departments with an above average number of discrete treatment areas which are not inter-visible are likely to require high staffing budgets.

Short-stay wards: A&E budgets may include the cost of nursing patients on short-stay or admissions wards, many of whom may have been admitted under other specialties, and of any drugs and investigations which they are given. This expenditure should be reported separately on trust financial returns, but apportionment is sometimes crude. Short-stay patients, particularly those admitted to observation wards, are not always counted, and treatment of 'lodged' patients awaiting an inpatient bed likewise varies.

The boundaries of A&E: Each hospital has a somewhat different policy and practice as to the stage at which specialties become involved with A&E patients.

Peripheral A&Es: The apparent costs of major A&E units may be distorted by the inclusion of peripheral A&E or minor injuries units with very different cost structures. Some major A&E departments also supplement the staffing of these minor units on a rota basis or provide supervision, increasing their reported unit costs. Conversely, at some small hospitals, patients with minor injuries are treated by outpatient nurses who are not costed to A&E.

Extra doctors: At some sites studied, certain senior A&E doctors are paid by an academic institution and are not costed to A&E.

Shared staff: A&E departments may share staff with other specialties. Plaster technicians and outpatient nurses may help out as nursing auxiliaries in A&E when they are not busy. At certain times of day, A&E reception may be staffed by relief clerks from medical records who are not costed to A&E budgets. Conversely, A&E receptionists may also be required to carry out medical records work. A&E managers, too, may supervise a number of other departments.

Apportionment of clinical overheads: There is wide variation between trusts as to whether costs of drugs dispensed to A&E patients by pharmacy, radiology, pathology, computers or security are included in departmental budgets or apportioned subsequently as overheads. The ways in which these clinical support costs should be allocated between departments on trust financial returns are specified in the NHS Manual of Accounts. However, most hospitals base the apportionment on historical samples of each department's usage. Thus, for example, if an A&E reduces its number of X-ray requests, it may be several years before this saving is reflected in its specialty costs.

Trust overheads: This is usually the biggest and most variable element of reported A&E specialty expenditure, but lies almost entirely outside the control of the A&E department.

Differences in the percentage composition of reported A&E specialty costs at different hospitals illustrate the effect of these distortions (Exhibit 27). Consider two of those studied: one has specialty costs per A&E attendance which are 61 per cent higher than the other, but both its A&E budgets and its pay costs per attender are 28 per cent lower. At some hospitals, continuing pressure from purchasers to reduce costs and the way budgets are allocated between departments can affect clinical practice. For instance, A&E staff may be unwilling to administer expensive drugs, waiting for them to be prescribed by specialty doctors, so they are attributed to the specialty budget. In one hospital, blood tests are also left for the specialty doctor. Such delays are not in the interest of patients.

Exhibit 27
Composition of A&E gross specialty unit costs at study sites

Differences in the percentage composition of reported A&E specialty costs at different hospitals serve to illustrate the effect of distortions in the calculation of unit costs.

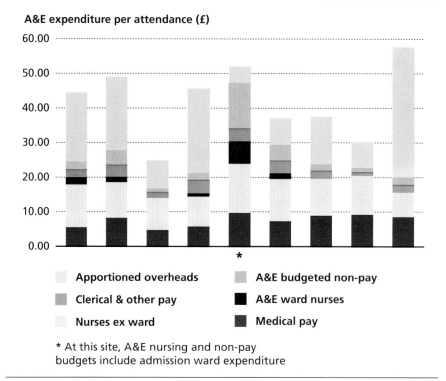

A&E expenditure per attendance (£)

Apportioned overheads   A&E budgeted non-pay

Clerical & other pay   A&E ward nurses

Nurses ex ward   Medical pay

* At this site, A&E nursing and non-pay budgets include admission ward expenditure

Source: Audit Commission site visits

Appendix 3: The National Audit Office Report on A&E Departments

The main findings and conclusions of the 1992 National Audit Office report on NHS Accident and Emergency Departments in England (Ref. 1) were as follows:

Severe injuries:

◆ Early and continuing improvements are needed to ensure uniformly good provision for care of all severely injured patients.

◆ The Department of Health and the NHS should consider how trauma audit should be carried forward.

Medical staffing:

◆ Forecasts of appointments of an additional 72 A&E consultants in England in the three years to the end of 1995 are consistent with NAO findings that experienced medical staff in A&E are often over-stretched. New posts should be deployed to achieve the greatest benefits to quality of service for patients. Potential benefits of the increased staffing include better training and supervision of inexperienced doctors.

Planning and strategic issues:

◆ Regions (now regional offices of the NHS Executive) need to develop policy frameworks (eg, for location of A&E departments).

◆ Purchasers need to continue to develop quality standards linked to contractual targets.

◆ Concerted action is needed to ensure that patients receive the most appropriate health care and that departments are not overloaded with patients who might be better treated elsewhere.

◆ Numbers of return attendances could be further reduced in some places.

More positive management:

◆ There should be stronger representation of A&E departments in hospital management.

◆ More flexible and capable computerised management information systems are needed – paving the way for objective assessment of the efficiency and effectiveness of the departments' work.

◆ Measures are needed to improve management of the departments' rising workload.

◆ There should be consistently better use of nurses' skills.

◆ The adequacy and timeliness of support to the departments from other specialties and services should be monitored.

◆ Better communications with general practitioners are needed.

◆ Systematic clinical audit should be developed.

Appendix 4: The Clinical Standards Advisory Group Report on Urgent and Emergency Admissions to Hospital

The recommendations of the CSAG report (Ref. 3) can be summarised as follows:

◆ National guidelines should be developed for the emergency services under the auspices of the Royal Colleges and the Health Departments. These should relate to timeliness ... access, availability, effectiveness and quality. These should be incorporated into standards agreed in local protocols and contracts by purchasing authorities.

◆ Health authorities should examine their arrangements and hospitals their procedures urgently to seek necessary improvements in timing of key events in the admission of urgent or emergency patients.

◆ Hospitals should review the management arrangements for urgent or emergency admission including:

– bed ownership;

– observation and admissions wards and their optimum organisation;

– emergency operating theatres;

– problems which result from bed closures;

– bed managers and discharge co-ordinators;

– further development of clinical directorates;

– communications within hospital;

– nursing and other professional staffing;

– availability of support services.

◆ Consideration should be given to placing all acute specialties on a single site.

◆ All A&E departments should be led by a consultant trained in A&E medicine.

◆ Inadequate medical establishment should be resolved by increasing the number of training posts.

◆ Handover arrangements should be agreed so that patients may be admitted without repeated examination by junior trainees (from other departments).

- ◆ Problems that some general practices have in providing a 24-hour service should be addressed by FHSAs.

- ◆ Further evaluation of nurse practitioner schemes in A&E should be undertaken.

- ◆ Substantive arrangements should be developed in consultation with psychiatrists to deal with problems associated with psychiatric patients in A&E departments.

- ◆ Solutions should be sought urgently to counter discharge delays attributable to social services or community care. Closer consultation should be developed.

- ◆ Purchasers should contract for and hospitals should receive appropriate funding for the provision of emergency services according to activity and quality.

- ◆ Contracts should provide... for variations in demand... and in place.

- ◆ Initiatives such as those to reduce elective waiting lists should be implemented in a way that does not adversely affect the emergency services.

Appendix 5: Indicators of an Effective, User-friendly A&E Service

The NHS Executive has issued the following guidance:

- The department is consultant-led with appropriately trained staff, is open 24 hours a day, seven days a week, all the year round and has support and back-up at all times from appropriate clinical specialties.

- The department is clearly identifiable and easily accessible by all, including those with special needs, e.g. elderly people and people with disabilities.

- The patient receives an immediate clinical assessment by a suitably trained health professional.

- Patients with life-threatening illnesses or injuries are treated immediately.

- Waiting times are kept to a minimum, with the time for patients in a less critical situation based on their individual needs.

- Assessment and treatment is undertaken in privacy and with respect for the patient's dignity.

- The department is clean, well-maintained and with sufficient facilities, such as pay-phones, public toilets with facilities for people with disabilities.

- There are separate waiting space, play facilities and examination and recovery rooms furnished and equipped to meet children's and infants' needs in safe conditions.

- Patients, visitors and staff are protected from violence or harassment whilst in the department.

- A named nurse is identified, who provides continuity of care for the patient and relatives.

- Patients, and their relatives, are informed about anticipated waiting times, diagnosis, treatment and so on.

- Other relevant material is available and easily accessible, e.g. health promotion literature, a hostel directory for homeless people and advice on registering with a GP.

- Proper provision is made for patients with mental health needs and those who deliberately self-harm.

- The patient's location within the accident and emergency department is recorded and monitored by those in charge of the department.

Appendix 6: The Audit Commission Report on Care of Elderly Patients with Hip Fracture

A number of the findings of the Audit Commission Report: *United They Stand: Co-ordinating Care for Elderly Patients with Hip Fracture* relate to A&E departments.

Most people who fracture a hip are elderly. Almost all are admitted via A&E departments. Patients often wait several hours on trolleys while a full assessment is completed and admission arrangements are made. The Royal College of Physicians' guidelines recommend that hip fracture patients should not spend more than one hour in A&E. Staff in all of the hospitals visited agreed in principle with this recommendation, but most patients (96 per cent of those studied) waited longer than an hour.

Many elderly hip fracture patients arriving in A&E have already spent some time undiscovered on the floor at home. Because of the changes associated with ageing, this leaves them vulnerable to pain, confusion and dehydration, all of which may result in longer stays and poorer outcomes.

In addition, older patients are particularly vulnerable to pressure sores, which can start to develop in as little as 30 minutes and may already be present when the patient is admitted. Pressure sore risk should always be assessed as soon as possible in A&E, and immediate prevention and care carried out.

Many patients find busy A&E departments overwhelming, and older people are particularly vulnerable. Most A&E departments do not have immediate access to expertise in elderly care or social care assessment. Without early assessment vital information may be missed. People arriving at A&E are often accompanied by a friend, relative or neighbour who can provide extra information; and ambulance staff are often able to comment on home circumstances. Wherever possible, this information should be recorded, and either acted upon immediately (e.g. where patients are caring for someone older than frailer than themselves at home) or passed on to others who will be responsible for planning the eventual programme of rehabilitation.

Recommendations

Managers and doctors in acute hospitals should work together to:

i.   audit the time spent by hip fracture patients in A&E, and identify the reasons for delays in transferring patients to the wards.

ii. bring the radiology and orthopaedic staff together to review ways of speeding patients through the department, and agree:

  ◆ a waiting time standard for elderly patients in A&E, and

  ◆ procedures for the management of hip fractures on admission;

iii. review arrangements for caring for elderly people within A&E departments;

iv. ensure that all patients are assessed within an agreed time for pressure sore risk, and receive the necessary preventive care; and

v.   monitor these standards to see that they are met in practice.

They should aim to reduce the incidence of pressure sores by:

x.   reviewing pressure area care policies and procedures;

xi. developing systems to provide routine information on incidence and prevalence;

xii. auditing the use of assessment tools;

xiii. identifying and meeting training needs; and

xiv. ensuring that sufficient pressure relieving equipment is available.

Appendix 7: Improving the Care of Children in A&E

Effective treatment

◆ Effective treatment for children must be the first priority. There should be clear guidelines as to when A&E doctors should call for paediatric support.

◆ Protocols for pain control, with dosages for children of different weights and guidelines for conditions possibly requiring general anaesthesia, should be clearly displayed in A&E.

Child and family-centred care

◆ There should be a hospital-wide policy for child-centred care. Parents should be encouraged to remain with children while they are in A&E. Children attending A&E because another family member is sick or injured also need somewhere to wait separately from adult patients.

Specially skilled staff

◆ There should be a paediatrician on call to the department at all times of the day and night.

◆ One senior A&E doctor should take responsibility for promoting children's issues and ensuring that staff are trained in communicating with children and their parents.

◆ Hospitals should have a long-term plan for implementing the recommendation that there should be at least one child-trained nurse on duty in A&E at all times. This may not be possible in the short term, since there are currently insufficient child-trained nurses even to staff paediatric wards. Children's nurses transferring to A&E would also need to be able to treat adult patients, and few are likely to accept the lower grade typically offered while they gain this experience. But in the longer term, newly qualified child-branch nurses may seek jobs in A&E. In the interim, rotation of nurses with A&Es in children's hospitals could be explored; there might also be scope to rotate A&E nurses into paediatric wards. However, the most pressing need is for each A&E department to have at least one child-trained nurse with sufficient seniority to take the lead in raising awareness of children's issues.

Separate facilities

◆ Children should be able to wait and receive treatment in an environment which is safe, secure and non-threatening. There should be sufficient space for parents to be with the child at all times. At least one resuscitation space and one examination cubicle should be equipped for children.

Appropriate hospitalisation

◆ Inpatient treatment is a traumatic experience for a child and should be avoided if at all possible. Careful screening might substantially diminish the numbers of children admitted overnight. Admission procedures should ensure that children are referred rapidly to the appropriate specialty.

Non-accidental injuries

◆ All A&E doctors and nurses need to look out for any injuries to children, and to other vulnerable patients, which may not be accidental. Ready access to on-site paediatric advice is essential, but is not always available. Appropriate action and follow-up also requires close co-operation with health visitors, child protection teams and other social workers. Suspected abuse should be identified and followed up, preferably while the child is still at the hospital. Retrospective scrutiny of notes on young children attending A&E by a liaison health visitor can only be regarded as a long-stop. Liaison health visitors should visit the department and talk to A&E staff, since medical notes alone may be insufficient to alert them to possible abuse. A&E staff need guidance on those injuries or circumstances which should be considered suspicious in children and adolescents within particular age ranges. There should be procedures enabling doctors and senior nurses to gain swift access at any time of the day and night to child protection registers, including those for other areas.

Appendix 8: Co-location of Specialties and Supporting Services with A&E Departments

Many previous reports have recommended which specialties and services should be available on an A&E site. Examples include:

	RCS	BOA	CSAG
Anaesthesia	E (*)	Yes *	Yes
Emergency Medicine	E (*)		
General Medicine		Yes	Yes
General Surgery	E (*)	Yes *	Yes
Orthopaedic Surgery	E (*)	Yes *	Yes
Cardiology	E		(Yes)
Geriatrics			Yes
Gynaecology			Yes
Psychiatry			Yes
Respiratory Medicine	E		
Intensive Therapy/Care	D (*)	Yes	Yes
Paediatrics	D (E)	Yes	Yes
Maxillo-facial Surgery	D (E)	A (Yes)	
Nephrology	D (E)		
Ophthalmic Surgery	D (E)		
Otorhinolaryngological Surgery	D (E)		
Paediatric Surgery	D (E)		
Plastic Surgery	D (E)	- (Yes)	
Urological Surgery	D (E)		(Yes)
Gastroenterology	D		
Neurosurgery	- (E)	- (Yes)	
Cardiothoracic Surgery	- (D)	- (Yes)	

By Accident or Design
Improving A&E Services in England and Wales

	RCS	BOA	CSAG
Operating Theatre – fully staffed and available 24 hours a day	D (E)	Yes	Yes
Radiology (Diagnostic and Interventional)	E		
24-hour diagnostic services			Yes
24-hour radiography		Yes	
CT Scanning	D (E)	Yes +	
Angiography/Ultrasound/Nuclear Medicine	D (E)		
Bacteriology	E		
Chemical Pathology	E		
Haematology	E		
24-hour blood transfusion service		Yes	

Sources:

RCS: *Royal College of Surgeons of England: Report of the Working Party on the Management of Patients with Major Injuries (November 1988): Appendix 2 – Optimum Staff Requirements for Trauma Centres and District General Hospitals Receiving Injured Patients*
E Essential at a DGH, D   Desirable at a DGH
Letters in brackets refer to additional requirements of trauma/major injury centres
* A trauma centre would require 24 hours a day resident consultant availability

BOA: *British Orthopeadic Association: The Management of Skeletal Trauma in the United Kingdom (November 1992):*
BOA recommendations for Designated District Accident Centres
(A: 'either on-site or readily available')
Additional requirements for Regional Accident Centres are bracketed
* Consultant immediately available while on duty at Regional Accident Centre
+ On-line to regional neurological service.

CSAG: *Clinical Standards Advisory Group: Urgent and Emergency Admissions to Hospital (January 1995): Para. 5.5.1.4, etc.*
'The siting of any of these (specialties) in a hospital different from the one in which the A&E department is situated may delay admission and the management of emergencies in these specialties.'

Appendix 9: Advantages and Disadvantages of Admissions Wards

A number of advantages, disadvantages and issues to be considered when evaluating admissions wards were discussed in the Audit Commission report, 'Lying in Wait: The Use of Medical Beds in Acute Hospitals' (Ref. 26):

Advantages

- They 'buy time' to find the most suitable bed;
- On-take firms know where all new patients are;
- They prevent disturbance at night of patients sleeping on the main wards;
- The staffing requirements on all wards tend to be more stable;
- They eliminate the practice of discharging patients for a future take;
- They aid the planning of work on the main wards;
- They act as a filter to inappropriate admission;
- They allow for better use of split sites;
- The concentration of expertise can improve the quality of care of acutely ill patients.

Disadvantages

- Beds are further sub-divided;
- One transfer is inevitable – a particular problem for elderly patients;
- They run counter to the concept of primary nursing;
- Staff on main wards may feel devalued.

Issues

- Deciding on the correct size of the admissions ward;
- Strong management is essential to ensure that patients are transferred promptly from the ward;
- Nurse staffing must be adjusted to reflect the lower intensity of treatment on other wards.

Thus, in terms of quality of nursing care, admissions wards are necessarily second best, unless used only for admissions at night. A patient does not retain the same named nurse throughout their stay in hospital and information important to care planning and the possibility of a stress-free hospital stay may be lost unless nursing documentation is meticulous. Some patients find mixed-sex wards distressing. However, the advantages of enhanced levels of medical cover and more flexible management of beds may outweigh these considerations.

Appendix 10: Advantages and Disadvantages of Three Forms of Minor Injuries Service

Three models of minor injuries units, with differing levels of medical involvement, are currently in operation. Each has its strengths and weaknesses.

(1) Nurse-led minor injuries services within A&E

PROS	CONS
Decreases waiting times.	There is a possibility of staff being called away to major cases.
Maintains the flow of patients, even if the 'major' area of the department is busy.	
Safety: there is a medical presence at all times.	Protocols may be unnecessarily restricted because doctors are always present.
There is likely to be emphasis on audit and training.	Unless nurses rotate to other jobs, they may loose their broader A&E skills.
Financial: there are fewer building cost implications than stand-alone minor injuries unit.	Treatment of minor injuries will have to bear a share of high hospital overhead costs.
Improved liaison with other specialists if these are on site.	There is a possibility of attracting more patients who would otherwise self-care or see their GP.
Patients retain the choice of seeing a doctor or a nurse.	Two tier system: patients are not prioritised strictly according to clinical need.

(2) Stand-alone, with medical presence

PROS	CONS
Public support, convenience, and accessibility.	Likely to be an unattractive career option for doctors and inconvenient for GPs.
The medical presence increases public *perceptions* of their safety.	There is a greater possibility that seriously ill or injured patients who could not be treated properly in this setting might attend.
	There is unlikely to be any ongoing training for nurses, unless rotations with other hospitals are established.
There is a possibility of decreased waiting times.	Often nurses work autonomously without accreditation.
Patients are given the choice to see a doctor or a nurse.	There is likely to be a lack of continuing training and accreditation for doctors.
Financial: cheaper if set up within existing premises.	Financial: A&E staff costs (depending on grades at which they are employed).

(3) Stand-alone, nurse led

PROS	CONS
Public support, convenience and accessibility.	To operate safely, these need:
May provide a facility where A&E services are being closed down.	◆ tight protocols, regularly updated ◆ links to A&E, consultant support
Models are already up and running and have been shown to function well.	◆ consultant radiologist support ◆ audit ◆ nurse practitioners with proven capabilities.
Decreased waiting times.	Patients are not given the choice to see a doctor, other than by travelling.
These units attract high calibre nurses and are good for nurse development.	Nurses could lose their broader A&E skills, unless rotations to major A&E departments are established.
There is the opportunity to develop inter-specialty links.	
There could be financial benefits, if existing premises are used…	…but the running costs may be high.

References

1. National Audit Office: *NHS Accident and Emergency Departments in England* (1992) HMSO 158.

2. National Audit Office: *NHS Accident and Emergency Departments in Scotland* (1992) HMSO 159.

3. Clinical Standards Advisory Group: *Urgent and Emergency Admissions to Hospital* (1995) HMSO.

4. Standing Medical Advisory Committee: *Accident and Emergency Services (Platt Report)* (1962) HMSO.

5. British Association for Accident and Emergency Medicine: *Directory 1993.* Royal College of Surgeons of England.

6. NHS Trust Federation in association with the King's Fund: *Analysing Changes in Emergency Medical Admissions* (1995) NHSTF.

7. Department of Health: *The Patient's Charter* (1992) HMSO.

8. British Association for Accident and Emergency Medicine: *Medical Staffing: Accident and Emergency Departments* (1993).

9. Department of Health, report of the working group on specialist medical training: *Hospital Doctors: Training for the Future (Calman Report)* (1993) Department of Health.

10. Dale J, Green J, Glucksman E, Higgs R: *Providing for Primary Care: Progress in A&E: Report of the King's College Hospital Accident and Emergency Primary Care Project* (1991) King's College School of Medicine & Dentistry – Department of General Practice and Primary Care; King's College Hospital – Department of Accident and Emergency Medicine.

11. Burke D P, Rashid N: Primary Care in Accident and Emergency Departments: Cost of Employing General Practitioners in Department May Outweigh Savings (letter) *British Medical Journal* (1995) 311:1438.

12. Read S M, Jones N M B, Williams B T: 'Nurse Practitioners in Accident and Emergency Departments: What Do They Do?' (1992) *British Medical Journal*, 305:1466-70.

13. Jones, G J: *The Value of Initial Patient Assessment within the Accident and Emergency Department and the Most Effective Way of Achieving this Activity* (1995) Department of Health, Patient's Charter Unit [unpublished].

14. North East Thames RHA: *Accident and Emergency Services – A Guide to Good Practice* (2 Vols for Purchasers and for Providers) (1992) NETRHA.

15. South East Thames RHA: *Service Standards: Accident and Emergency Services* (1993) SETRHA.

16. Trent Health: *Focus on Accident and Emergency – An Aid to Contracting* (1992) Trent RHA.

17. British Orthopaedic Association: *The Management of Skeletal Trauma in the United Kingdom* (1992) British Orthopaedic Association.

18. Audit Commission: *United They Stand: Co-ordinating Care for Elderly Patients with Hip Fracture* (1995) HMSO.

19. Audit Commission: *Children First: A Study of Hospital Services* (1993) HMSO.

20. Royal College of Nursing A&E Nursing Forum and Society of Paediatric Nursing: *Nursing Children in the Accident and Emergency Department* (1990) Royal College of Nursing.

21. Department of Health: *Welfare of Children and Young People in Hospital* (1991) HMSO.

22. National Association for the Welfare of Sick Children in Hospital: *The NAWCH Charter* (1984).

23. British Association for Accident and Emergency Medicine and Royal College of Nursing: *Bereavement Care in A&E Departments: Report of the Working Group* (1995) RCN.

24. NHS Executive: *Accident and Emergency Departments* (1994) Department of Health (Leeds).

25. Gaskell D J, Crosby D L, Fenn N, James R L, Lewis P A, Rees B I, Roberts C J, Roberts S M: *Improving the Primary Management of Emergency Surgical Admissions: A Controlled Trial* (1995) Bulletin of the Annals of the Royal College of Surgeons of England.

26. Audit Commission: *Lying in Wait: The Use of Medical Beds in Acute Hospitals* (1992) HMSO.

27. Royal College of Surgeons (Irving M – Chairman): *Report of the Working Party on the Management of Patients with Major Injuries* (1988) Royal College of Surgeons of England.

28. Campling E A, Devlin H B, Hoile R W, Lunn J N: *The Report of the National Confidential Enquiry into Perioperative Deaths* (1989) Royal College of Surgeons of England.

29. London Implementation Group, A&E Reference Group: *Accident and Emergency Services: The Desired Standard* (1993).

30. North West Thames RHA: *Accident and Emergency Task Force* (1992).

31. Baker B: 'Model Methods', *Nursing Times* (24 Nov 1993) Vol 89, No. 47, 33-35.

32. Rich G: *A Study of Minor Injury Services* (1994) NHS Executive.

33. Read S: *Patients with Minor Injuries: A Literature Review of Options for Their Treatment Outside Major Accident and Emergency Departments or Occupational Health Settings* (1994) Trent Institute for Health Services Research.

34. Hertfordshire Health Agency: *Towards a Healthier Hertfordshire: A&E Services Review: Technical Document* (1994) Hertfordshire Health Agency.

35. Dale J, Dolan B, Lang H: *Healthcare in Folkestone and Deal: New Directions for the Minor Injuries Units* (1994) King's A&E Primary Care Service and Kent FHSA.

36. Dale J, Rennie D, Roberts J, Tyson L: *Minor Injuries Services: A Major Public Concern: An Option Appraisal for Bromley Health* (1994) King's College School of Medicine & Dentistry – Department of General Practice & Primary Care.

37. Mirfin S M: *An Examination of the Costs and Demand for Minor Injuries Units in Barking and Havering Health Authority* (1994) Project submitted in part fulfilment of the requirements of the Chartered Institute of Public Finance & Accountancy Professional Examination 3.

38. Winkler F: *Briefing Paper: Visit of the London Implementation Group to the Association of the Medway Doctors-on-Call* (1993) [unpublished].

39. Goldie P: 'Out-of-hours Plan Stresses Teamwork', *Hospital Doctor* (4 May 1995).

40. Dale J, D'Souza P: *Primary Care in A&E: Establishing the Service: A User's Guide to Planning, Commissioning and Providing an Accident and Emergency Primary Care Service* (1992) King's College Hospital – Department of Accident and Emergency Medicine, King's College School of Medicine and Dentistry – Department of General Practice and Primary Care.

41. NHS Executive: *Opportunities in Emergency Health Care: Summary Report from the Anglia and Oxford Emergency Health Care Project* (1995) NHS Executive, Anglia & Oxford Region.

42. NHS Executive: *Emergency Care Handbook* (1995) NHS Executive: Anglia & Oxford Region.

43. Irving M, Heatley F W: *Review of Accident and Emergency, Trauma and Orthopaedic Services in Leeds* (1995) NHS Executive: Northern and Yorkshire Region.

Index References are to paragraph numbers